INCIDENT AT
DEVILS DEN

A True Story, by
TERRY LOVELACE, ESQ.
—————— Former ——————
Assistant Attorney General

COMPELLING PROOF OF ALIEN VISITATION

ALLEGED GOVERNMENT INVOLVEMENT AND

AN ALIEN IMPLANT

DISCOVERED ON A ROUTINE X-RAY

Guest appearances
Midnight in the Desert with Heather Wade
Veritas with Mel Fabregas, *veritasradio.com*
FATE Radio with Todd Bates

ISBN-13: 978-0692072011
ISBN-10: 0692072012

Editor: George Verongos

For Sheila

TABLE OF CONTENTS

Preface

Devils Den State Park in Northwestern Arkansas is a beautiful place. Folks who love the outdoors can appreciate its near perfection. But, beneath the scenic forests and limestone outcroppings there lies a mystery. People from Devils Den go missing. A lot of people. Those missing souls go somewhere. The mystery is where?

Devils Den is considered cursed ground by local Native Americans. Caddo and Cahinno tribes treat the land with measured deference and have done so as far back as anyone can recall. I wondered if Neolithic people felt uneasy when they walked these trails? In 1977 I couldn't shake the feeling someone was behind me. It was unnerving.

The Butterfield Trail that runs through the park is named after the Butterfield Stage Coach Line. The line operated from 1857 until hostilities between the States broke out in 1861. Horse-drawn coaches departed from hubs in St. Louis and Memphis, headed west to California. Their trek west took them through Devils Den along the trail that bears its name. The trail wound through some of the most in hospitable land imaginable.

Devils Den's history is rife with bloody skirmishes fought there during the civil war until the fighting ended in 1865. There is no written record of significant battles fought in Devils Den during the war. The dense underbrush and limestone summits were ideal for snipers. It was difficult terrain for either side to hold and likely considered not important enough to devote men to the effort.

Up until the late 1880s travelers through Devils Den were subject to attack by opposing Native Americans who resented the trespass. There were lawless times when travel carried great risks. In more recent times people just disappear.

In August 2017, Devils Den claimed a 33-year-old man from Bartlesville, Oklahoma. His story struck a chord of empathy in me. Rodney's case is an eerie tale. I'll just touch on the highlights. During a hiking trip along the Butterfield Trail, Rodney Letterman became separated from friends when he decided to remain at the campsite and rest instead of continuing the hike. When the others returned they found Rodney's cell phone. But Rodney Letterman had vanished. All that was found was the cellphone left lying at their campsite. Like most of us, I bet Mr. Letterman's cellphone rarely ever left his hand or his pocket.

Letterman's hometown paper, the *Bartlesville Examiner,* stated that as of December 2017, "Two thousand five hundred acres were searched," and except for his cellphone, nothing has ever been found of Rodney Letterman. The Washington County Arkansas Sheriff, John Shuster asked the public to help. He stated for the *Examiner*:

"All that we found was his cellphone ... We'd like to hear from anyone who might now (sic) something about the case."

I promise to keep readers apprised of developments in Mr. Letterman's case on my Facebook page, Incident at Devils Den. You may also check the Arkansas website at www.arkansasonline.com/news/2017/letterman.

Decades earlier, Devils Den also proved to be unlucky for an eight-year-old girl from Pennsylvania. In June 1946 the Van Alst family from Pittsburgh camped at Devils Den. The Van Alsts were a family of five. There was eight-year-old Kathryn, her parents and two brothers.

The precise details surrounding the day of her disappearance have been lost to time. It's known that Kathryn vanished from the family's campsite and a desperate search effort began. Details are scant, but Kathryn's disappearance was documented in the Van Alst family's hometown newspaper, the *Pittsburgh Press*.

In a story that ran June 24, 1946, the *Press* stated that after a week in the forest Kathryn was found. Her rescuer was identified as a search volunteer from the University of Arkansas, "19-year-old Chadwick." Chadwick was quoted as saying, "I called Kathryn's name and she walked out of a small cave dressed in her bathing suit and announced calmly, 'here I am.'"

In David Paulide's book *Missing 411*, he tells how Kathryn was found seven air miles and 600 feet elevation from the campsite. To reach that point would have required a twenty-mile trek on zigzagging trails and up rough terrain. Without shoes. The area where Chadwick found her had been previously searched. Twice. Once by air and again by volunteers.

What struck me as odd were quotes made in the *Press* by her rescuer, Chadwick and Kathryn's mother. The *Press* quoted "Chadwick" as describing Kathryn's demeanor as, "eerily calm."

When asked by the *Press,* Kathryn's mother described her daughter's mood as, "utterly serene."

The phrases "eerily calm" and "utterly serene" just seem out of context. It's puzzling to me.

Despite the absence of potable water anywhere near the site, Kathryn was found well hydrated and had not lost weight. She told her rescuers she could not recall how she got lost or what happened to her.

I tried to locate Chadwick through the University of Arkansas enrollment records and graduation records. Since it's unclear if Chadwick was a first or last name, it was difficult. The college also pointed out it may have been a student named Chadwick who chose to be called "Chad." If my name were Chadwick I'd prefer Chad.

I tried to locate Kathryn Van Alst who would now be seventy plus years of age. I was unsuccessful. It's an opportunity lost that she was never interviewed as an adult. I've thought about Kathryn often and wondered if Devils Den plagued Kathryn's sleep the way it's plagued mine for a half-century.

I'm grateful to have survived Devils Den. It cost my friend his life.

Introduction

I want to be clear from the start. I'm not on a mission to change your mind about the topic of UFOs or the existence of alien life. There are people like myself who've had experiences, and most spend an entire lifetime and never see a thing. I've never been a fan of science fiction. I don't read books about UFOs or any related topics. They disturb my sleep the way explicit crime novels keep my wife awake at night.

The genesis of this book is an event that occurred in 1977. While camping at a state park, a friend and I encountered an enormous UFO. It was triangular-shaped, and each side was approximately a city block in length. I'd estimate it was five stories tall with a matte black finish. All three corners were brilliantly lit from the bottom to the top with flashing multicolored lights.

It emitted a low drone. The noise was what you'd experience standing next to a very large piece of equipment like a diesel train engine. It was a bass tone that reverberated in your chest.

I'm a retired lawyer who spent many years in state government as a prosecutor and as an assistant attorney general. During my professional career, I didn't disclose these things for fear of losing my job and standing in the legal community. So, my wife and I kept these experiences to ourselves for 41 years. I planned to take the story to my grave.

Until 2012, when an anomalous piece of metal, found in my knee, changed things dramatically. That fingernail-sized piece of metal was the tipping point for me. It was the catalyst to write this book, speak publicly and make a full and candid disclosure of everything that's happened. My experiences with UFOs stretch back to my early childhood.

Why was I singled out for these four or five experiences over the span of a lifetime? I think it's because I was tagged. Like an animal on the Serengeti Planes of Africa.

This unexpected discovery motivated me to tell the world what happened to me nearly fifty years ago. It's difficult for me to accept that I have a metallic "thing" in my leg that medical science can't explain. The idea that nonhuman entities seized me and laid hands upon me makes my skin crawl. What happened to me may well have happened to you or someone you love. That "bad dream" you once had that seemed so real may not have been a nightmare. It may have been a memory.

If intelligent extraterrestrial beings are out there, then where are they? The United States Government steadfastly asserts that there's no proof of alien life anywhere on earth, or elsewhere in the universe. There's a new acronym to replace UFO. It's now UAP for, "Unknown Aerial Phenomena" in government circles. Whether UFOs or UAPs, the government claims it isn't interested.

The United States Government has no department or agency responsible for investigating UFO sightings. Citizens who wish to report a UFO are referred to their local law enforcement agency. Unless there's a crash involved, then it's an entirely different matter.

Imagine, on your drive home from work one afternoon, a silvery disc sails right over your car and abruptly stops in front of you. It's 50-feet, or less, overhead and you have a crystal-clear view. You pull over and watch. You're astounded! You wonder, "What is this thing?" Your mind races with possible explanations eliminating them one by one. This thing is big too. You'd estimate it to be 90 feet in diameter, bright, and shiny. Your peripheral vision notices that it casts an elliptical shadow to your left, consistent with the placement of the afternoon sun.

A couple of other cars have also pulled over. Other motorists are witnessing this too, so it can't be a product of your imagination. Some people have opened their car doors and are standing outside for a better look. Everyone is watching.

While you're fumbling around for your phone, the disc silently shoots upward and now sits motionless, parked 1,000-feet above you.

Afraid to look away for fear of missing something, you search for your phone by hand. By feel your hand finally grasps your phone. Taking your eyes off the disc for a split-second you make a quick glance at it to locate your camera icon. Before you can raise it to your eye, the disc darts off at incredible speed.

It vanishes in the blink of an eye. The entire event is over in less than 60 seconds. You're left standing by your car, stunned by what you've just experienced.

There's nothing wrong with your vision. You're sober and not a drug user. Remembering your high school physics, you know that the human body can't survive the g-forces in a vehicle accelerating to such speed.

You decide it's your duty to file a report with someone. To invoke a cliché, "Who you gonna call?" Surely, someone in government is responsible for investigating such things. Where do you start?

There's no real urgency, so you find a non-emergency telephone number for your local police and call. You're routed to a desk sergeant. You explain, "This isn't a true emergency, but I saw something very strange that I'd like to report, can you help? I saw a silver disc...."

As you're telling him about the disc you just witnessed and giving him the location, he interrupts you. "Madam," he asks, "has a crime been committed?"

"No. Not that I'm aware of … but."

He cuts you off for a second time, "I'm very sorry. We investigate crimes. If a crime hasn't been committed, I suggest you call the Air Force."

Still determined, you call the nearest United States Air Force base. After listening to a lengthy menu, you finally speak with the base operator.

"Hello, I'd like to file a UFO report please. May I speak to whoever handles UFO sightings?"

"One moment. I'll transfer you to an information officer." You're placed on hold while an instrumental rendition of "Off We Go into The Wild Blue Yonder" plays in the background.

The music ends and as a recruitment commercial begins a man picks-up. Without introduction and before you can get out a single word he tells you politely, "I'm sorry, we don't investigate UFO sightings."

Frustrated, you tell him, "I'm not asking for an investigation. I'd like to file a report; can you at least take a report for me?"

"No, I'm sorry, we don't take reports either. I suggest that you call your local law enforcement agency." Click. You realize you've just made a complete circle and you're now back where you began.

No one is interested in UFO reports or photographic images other than the MUFON people. MUFON stands for the Mutual UFO Network. It's a civilian run organization that collects and investigates UFO sightings across the United States and Canada. No one in government will accept this data so it's simply warehoused. Sometimes it's shared with civilian UFO investigators.

Our government's official policy is one of disinterest when it comes to civilian sightings of UFOs. Then why does it devote taxpayer dollars to fund the world's biggest search for intelligent extraterrestrial life. It sounds contradictory.

Chances are that you've heard of SETI. In case you're unfamiliar, SETI is the "Search for Extraterrestrial Intelligence." SETI has been listening for intelligent signals from space since the 1970s. Since 1993, the project has been funded by The United States Government through NASA. If you're curious, look at NASA's budget at the Office of Budget Management (OBM).

SETI uses several huge radio telescopes that scan the sky by night and by day listening for intelligent radio transmissions from anywhere in the cosmos. Their capabilities have greatly expanded since the project was first conceived in the 1970s. The growth of computer technology over the past 40 years allows SETI to search vast swathes of space that were previously unexplored.

SETI is not really a search for extraterrestrial intelligence. SETI is a search for radio signals, period. SETI is looking for analogue evidence in a digital age.

Our government's interest in SETI is to find proof that alien life exists. But not here. The goal is to shift public attention from what's over our heads to millions of miles away in deep space. The government might admit to proof of alien existence but only at arm's length. It is proof of their existence close to home that causes them discomfort. I'm reminded of a line from a movie where a police officer tries to disperse a crowd by saying, "Just move along folks, nothing to see here."

Joseph Goebbels said, "Given the proper psychology it would not be impossible to prove to the masses that a square is in fact a circle." History has proven him correct many times. The drumbeat to the masses in 2018? "Nasa's got everything under control. We're searching diligently for extraterrestrial life by scanning the skies for intelligent radio signals. Our land and orbital telescopes are discovering distant planets, new ones every day! Meticulously we are scanning the sky for radio waves. We're so close now!"

There are thousands of trustworthy people from all walks of life with reliable stories and incredible video evidence. Those sightings and witness reports, including film footage and photographs, are valuable. In the legal profession we call it evidence. The government directs our attention to outer space while the proof is in our own back yard. Sometimes literally.

At a Toronto conference in 2005, Paul Hellyer, a former Canadian Minister of Defence ("Defense" for US readers) announced publicly that UFOs and aliens exist. Unbelievably the world took little notice of his declaration. This was disclosure from a reliable person inside the highest echelon of government. Hellyer revealed that alien entities are here on earth and some even live among us. He claimed that aliens from distant stars visit earth regularly. Not one species of alien beings but perhaps a dozen! According to Hellyer, alien beings have been visiting earth for thousands of years. Outrageous claims by any standard. But given the credibility of the source, it's hard to dismiss.

In an article in the *Ottawa Citizen*, Hellyer "Demanded that world governments disclose what they know about their involvement with aliens." He said aliens possess the technology to reverse climate change and offer hundreds of other things that could benefit mankind. But world governments keep this information secret. These discoveries our government has locked-away. I wonder what marvelous secrets are locked away that could better the lives of everyone?

According to Hellyer, some world governments are in regular contact with ETs. He even claimed the United States Air Force works with aliens, side by side in the development of all manner of secret technology.

The world seems ready for full disclosure. If our government announced that intelligent alien beings are here and living among us it would be big news. But there'd be no rioting. There would be no frenzied crowds roaming the streets of New York and Hong Kong. No looting or global chaos would follow.

People are ready if not eager to hear the news. They've been ready for a hundred years. Intuitively, many people recognize that there are just too many sightings to deny their existence. Because sightings are now funneled to law enforcement agencies, I thought it wise to seek an opinion from a seasoned law enforcement officer. As a former district attorney, I have a few contacts in the legal community. I wanted to hear their perspective on UFOs. A Vermont police chief I've known for over a decade agreed to speak with me about his experiences. He was uncomfortable with the subject but agreed to a frank discussion so long as I respected his anonymity and didn't disclose his jurisdiction.

The chief admitted he has a file cabinet in his office devoted solely to UFO reports. He said, "It's damn near full. I hope there's enough room in the bottom drawer to see me to retirement." I asked him how long his agency had been compiling UFO reports. His answer surprised me. "My personal reports only go back about six years. I inherited the bulk of the files from my predecessor and from chiefs before them going back to the mid-1930s."

When I asked if he believes ETs visit earth, he didn't hesitate, "There's not a doubt in my mind. Now I personally have never seen a thing. But I have two deputies who claim they saw three cylinder-shaped objects fly across [location redacted]. My deputies were in different locations and in different vehicles. They reported their sightings to dispatch within minutes of each other. If they tell me they saw it, I believe them, … they were pretty shaken up about it too."

In 1899, Nicola Tesla, a brilliant and under-recognized genius of the early 20th century, claimed to have received a radio transmission from Mars. But Tesla lacked the credibility to back up his observation and conclusion. He needed evidence to support his claim. Without proof it was too extraordinary a statement to be believed. Tesla's claim underscores Carl Sagan's quote: "Extraordinary claims require extraordinary evidence."

Intelligent alien civilizations may intentionally choose to have an unlisted number. Announcing their presence by broadcasting into the vastness of space could have unwanted consequences. They might have well-reasoned motives to keep quiet and maintain a low profile. Perhaps they've learned a hard lesson we have yet to learn.

No one else in the universe may be broadcasting. But we sure are. We've been unwittingly announcing our presence to the universe for seventy-five years. "The Twilight Zone" has been traveling across the cosmos at the speed of light since the 1950s.

More concerning to many is that SETI is not just devoted to listening. SETI has been actively broadcasting messages into space since 1974. SETI's signals are much more powerful than a 1950's television broadcast. In 2008, SETI and its partners beamed a powerful signal into deep space. It was pointed toward a region believed most likely to be inhabitable. What was their message? It was a Beatle tune from 1970 by John Lennon, "Across the Universe."

We are shouting into the darkness.

In 2015, Stephen Hawking cautioned the world against broadcasting high-energy radio signals into space. Our broadcasts are targeted toward galaxies we believe could support intelligent life. Hawking warned, "When an advanced civilization meets a less advanced civilization our world had proven it will not go well for the less advanced civilization." I'm sure his words strike a chord of empathy with Native Americans.

Bill Gates and Elon Musk joined with Hawking to warn against advertising our existence. Collectively they concluded we could be inviting beings that are not benign space brothers.

The wording is clumsy, but the message is clear. In 2006 an article published in the respected scientific journal *Nature* warned that the risk posed by SETI broadcasts is real. The article cautioned that world contact with extraterrestrial entities, even benign ones, could have "serious repercussions." Nearly a decade before Stephen Hawking's warning other academics reached the same conclusion and raised the alarm.

If contacted, they may not offer us technology and scientific advancement for free. There may be a quid pro quo. But the terms may not be to our liking. They may not barter at all. They might just take whatever they like. Our signals could be intercepted by intergalactic opportunists. Malevolent beings well organized and seeking new worlds to pillage could well be listening. Their agenda could be to enslave the unfortunate inhabitants of less sophisticated worlds or maybe worse. It rings of science fiction but it's worth contemplation.

We take for granted human qualities like mercy, empathy, love, and ethics. We assume compassion will advance at the same rate as technology. Unfortunately, mankind's history doesn't support that assertion. The genocidal atrocities of the twentieth century are a compelling testament to mankind's failure to advance. In a world of plenty, millions struggle to survive without adequate nutrition, medical care and education.

Alien entities might view our world as so unsophisticated that human life is insignificant to them. They may treat us the way we treat microbes under a microscope slide. They might destroy civilizations the same way we discard a petri dish loaded with living spores. It's a sobering thought.

The oldest documented UFO sighting I can find is from almost 3,500 years ago. It occurred in the year 1440 BCE. "Fiery discs in the sky" were seen over Southern Egypt and were recorded by Thutmose III's scribes. Contemporaneously and independently, the same sightings were also recorded in the Tulli papyrus.

This was a UFO sighting made by two independent witnesses unknown to each other and separated by distance. Sightings with two or more independent witnesses are more believable. Probably the best example was the Phoenix, Arizona mass sighting in 1997.

On March 13, 1997, thousands of residents of Phoenix reported a very large, boomerang-shaped formation of lights over the Sierra Estrella Mountain Range. It's a curious coincidence that a bright comet named Hale-Bopp was crossing over Phoenix that same evening. This accounts for the staggering number of Arizonians that were watching the sky that night. Everyone was hoping for a glimpse of the comet. What most saw was something completely different.

Witnesses reported a "string of light" miles across and moving in perfect unison more like an enormous single object. They claimed that between the lights the stars were blotted out of the night sky as the object past overhead. All the witnesses swore that what they witnessed was a single enormous object instead of a string of lights.

The United States Air Force claimed the lights were flares dropped by aircraft during a routine exercise. That explanation was debunked. The Air Force takes all atmospheric conditions into consideration before planning an exercise over a populated area. It's common practice to make a press release in advance so folks can expect to see something odd in the night sky. We are to believe the USAF scheduled an exercise that involved dropping brilliant flares on the same night and the same time that a comet was due to traverse the Phoenix sky? It's hard for me to believe.

I guess I'm an unapologetic conspiracy theorist. I believe the United States Government is a party to the process. They work collaboratively to advance an agenda that will become known to all of us who live long enough. As a lawyer, I've been trained to collect and present evidence. I intend to present my experiences to you truthfully and without embellishment. Take from it what you will and if nothing else, please enjoy the story of my misfortune.

We have already opened our doors to monsters. They have arrived.

A Souvenir

How is running relevant to alien implants? For me, there's a solid connection between the two. It's where this story begins. My life might have been different if I had paid attention to a subtle clue my body gave me in 1980.

In the early 80s, I was caught up in a fad known as "jogging." President Jimmy Carter touted the benefits of non-competitive running. Athletic celebrities like Steve Prefontaine and Joan Benoit promoted running for its health benefits. It's hard today to think of running as something new.

In the 60s, we wore generic athletic sneakers. By the 1970s, Nike and others introduced new products engineered for runners and marketed to runners. Jogging began as a fad, but over time it gained momentum as a healthy lifestyle. I ran for the cardiovascular benefit and became hooked on the endorphins.

My father was a product of the depression era and WWII. Pragmatic to a fault in so many ways he was a staunchly purpose-driven man. He held onto his beliefs from the 1930s until he passed away. I regret I never had the opportunity to ask his opinion of paying $2.00 for a bottle of tap water or $5.00 for a cup of coffee.

In his later years, once or twice a week, we'd meet just to talk. At his kitchen table in our old home, we'd share a pot of coffee. The topic of our discussion one day was my new hobby. I was excited to tell him about jogging and explain its many benefits. Today we merely refer to it as running.

He chuckled and lit a cigarette. "Why the hell do you want to run if no one's chasing you?" Silly as it sounds, his question was genuine.

"Pop, it's a good way to exercise and control my weight."

"You gain weight because you eat too damn much!"

"Point taken, Pop. But for me, it's better to burn off calories and enjoy the cardiovascular benefits as a bonus. You know coronary artery disease runs in our family."

"This jogging. It's a fad. You'll spend money on fancy shoes, and a month later you'll be on to some other business," Pop said in that way only men over 70 can say.

"Maybe so Pop, but I like it, and it can't hurt me," I said.

"Oh yes! You're going to hurt yourself! You could trip on the sidewalk and break a leg or get hit by a car," he cautioned. "Then what happens if you can't work?"

The concept of running purely for pleasure was a hard idea to wrap his head around. Competitive running was a legitimate sport and served a purpose. Running away from something or someone that threatened your life was valid because that also served a purpose. He saw running in the military akin to marching. Something that was done for discipline and fitness for battle, it served a purpose. But running as a civilian?

I gave it some reflection. Look through all the old photographs and motion pictures depicting life in the United States pre-1970. I dare you to find a single picture of someone running who's not on an athletic field or running away from something.

Finding a safe place to run presented a problem. Pop was right about that, our old South St. Louis neighborhood was in decline. Running on city streets meant dodging cars and outrunning dogs. There were also the occasional jeers.

As I built up my endurance, I worked my way from one mile a day to a mile-and-a-half and then two. The first time I hit that two-mile mark I noticed something odd. It'd never happened before. Just above my right knee was a spot about the size of a half-dollar that tingled and was numb. With a pin, I could trace its borders. It had a clearly defined edge. This numb spot made no sense to me. Like clockwork, it appeared every time I hit that two-mile mark within a hundred or so yards. But it never interfered with my life or my running.

I asked around. None of my fellow runners had ever experienced anything like it. My doctor's advice was, "If it doesn't hurt, don't worry about it." He just blew it off and encouraged me to do the same.

Running became a habit and, at times, an obsession for the next 40 years. Throughout all those years, after every run, the numb spot appeared without exception. It would last for an hour or so after each run and then fade away. On rare occasions it appeared even when I wasn't running. Usually at times when I was under extreme stress.

On the morning of October 23, 2012, I woke up to find I couldn't bear weight on my right leg. My right knee was so painful I couldn't walk. It hadn't bothered me the day before. But now I could barely stand, and I fell trying.

Placing even a small amount of weight on my leg was incredibly painful at the knee. My wife drove me to the VA Hospital to have it checked out. I didn't believe my leg could be broken since I hadn't taken a hard fall or experienced any other kind of accident.

The emergency room meant a three-hour wait. I understand heart attack victims take priority over a bad knee. I was eventually checked in and examined by a physician assistant. She was kind and seemed very knowledgeable. Even though I hadn't suffered a severe injury, she ordered an x-ray and I was wheeled off and onto the table.

The x-ray technician positioned my leg and took two views of my knee. One view from front to back and another from the side. Five minutes later she came back and took two more. She seemed puzzled and repeated the process a third time and then a fourth. That made a total of eight ex-rays.

The technician asked, "Mr. Lovelace, did you suffer a shrapnel wound while in the military or have you been an accident of some kind?"

Curious, I answered after a few seconds of thought, "No, never."

"Other than the fall you took this morning, are you sure you never injured that leg in the past? Maybe a car accident many years ago?" she asked.

"No. May I ask why?" I was puzzled too and wondering where this line of questioning was headed. "I've never been in any kind of accident or injured my leg in the past. I used to be a runner, but that never caused problems with my knee."

She explained, "There's a tiny object just above your knee that looks metallic. It's the same density as metal. I've asked the radiologist to give his opinion. He should be down in just a minute," she said.

I asked, "May I see the x-rays, and can I speak with radiologist please?" The numb spot never crossed my mind.

The x-ray technician left the room. A few minutes later she returned with the physician assistant and the radiologist. The radiologist also brought his resident along. Soon, the x-ray room became crowded as other medical people trickled in. All were eager for a look at my x-ray.

The radiologist asked, "Mr. Lovelace, I see what looks like a tiny piece of square metal in your right leg just above your knee."

"Doctor, that's news to me."

The radiologist carefully examined my knee and lower thigh. After a few minutes he shook his head and admitted, "I don't see it. It should be right here," he said, poking my thigh with his finger.

"What should be right there?" I asked.

"A point of entry."

"What do you mean by a point of entry?" I asked.

"I mean there should be a scar where this piece of metal pierced your skin and entered your thigh. After years they can sometimes be hard to see. But there's always one there. Maybe you suffered an accident in early childhood or some other injury that you forgot about? It could have happened when you were too young to remember. I want to examine your knee under a black light, scar tissue will fluoresce under a black light."

He flipped off the overhead lights and examined every inch of my knee with his handheld black light. After ten minutes of looking he asked his intern to see if she could find a scar. After another ten-minute examination, she reached the same conclusion. There was no scar to be found. There is no scar.

The radiologist was overtly shocked, "Mr. Lovelace you have a very unusual knee," he said.

Now, more curious than ever, I asked, "Doctor how often do you find a foreign object under the skin without a corresponding scar?"

After a long pause he rubbed his chin and said, "Never... I've been in radiology for 23 years and I've never seen it before. It doesn't look like a shard of metal from an accident either. This object has symmetry to it ... it's definitely man-made."

His intern weighed-in, "These look like electrical leads of some kind," she said, using a pen as a pointer. The radiologist nodded affirmatively.

That was too difficult for me to process. I asked him to show me the x-rays and point out the object. He was quick to oblige. You didn't need a medical degree to see a square object that looked white in stark contrast to the dark x-ray film. It was about the size of a fingernail and just above my right knee imbedded in my thigh. I didn't make the connection until later. The metallic object was underneath the numb spot I experienced when I used to run.

"There's more," the radiologist added. He picked-up a second x-ray and popped it into the light box. "If you look at the lateral view below your knee, there's a flower petal arrangement of objects the same density as bone. These round artifacts are flat discs, so in the frontal view they're barely visible."

"Doctor, what's unusual about bones in my knee?" I asked, before I could get a close look at the film on the view box.

"These bones, if they are bones, are not in your knee. They're in the middle of your calf muscle. They're flat and not any type of cyst I'm familiar with. Cysts are round, fluid filled nodules, and these are discs. Also ... bone doesn't spontaneously sprout in the middle of muscle tissue! It's also odd that they are arranged with such symmetry."

The physician assistant said the metal fragment in my thigh was an oddity. But it wasn't the source of my knee pain. Her concerns were more immediate, people were piling up in the waiting room. She told me I was suffering from a Baker cyst. That was the cause of my pain. A Baker cyst has nothing to do with baking. It was discovered of course, by a man named Baker.

She told me, "They're always benign and resolve on their own in a couple weeks. There is no treatment other than rest." She was right. A few weeks later my knee was back to normal. Except that unexplained piece of metal was still under my skin.

There were two things I found disturbing. First, this metal object was directly over the numb spot, and secondly, the radiologist couldn't find a matching scar. That established a link between the metal thing and the numb spot on my knee.

It was the origin of the piece of metal in my knee that troubled me most. I checked with both of my older sisters. Except for the occasional skinned-knee in childhood, there was no accident that they knew of.

I wasn't obsessed by my knee. But I was close. A couple of weeks later I requested a copy of my x-rays from the VA. I requested copies of all eight x rays. The request took several weeks and a few telephone calls. But eventually, I got the films in digital form. I pulled the images up on my laptop and was intrigued. First, there were only two x-rays. An accompanying letter said the other films were discarded because of their poor quality. I studied both x-rays for thirty minutes. To think these things got under my skin somehow, made my skin crawl. What are they? Where did they come from? How did they find their way into my thigh?

Veterans Administration patients can access their medical records easily online. I only mention this to underscore that I had access to my medical history. Very convenient and relative to the facts as you'll see.

Despite my curiosity or perhaps out of dread, I hadn't read the radiologist's written report yet. I went online to pull up the report and the complete record from my emergency room visit of October 23. The doctor's note was what I expected. The PA had diagnosed my problem as a Baker cyst, but she made no mention of the mysterious objects.

The radiologist's report dated October 25, 2012, two days after my ER trip, acknowledged the objects below my knee and referred to them as "round artifacts." What he didn't mention in his report was the square metallic object that was clearly visible in the x-ray, just above my knee. Even though we openly discussed it! The report read simply "Impression: "ABNORMAL KNEE, Rule Out Baker Cyst."

My search engine found scarce mention of anything like what I have either above or below my knee. The closest images I found resembled alleged alien implants. I emphasize "alleged." Irrespective of their origin they now disturbed my sleep as well as my waking thoughts. I began having nightmares. Again.

After some diligent research, I found that the absence of scar tissue over a foreign object under the skin was a common denominator. It's the recognized hallmark of people with anomalies such as mine. Wherever these things came from I knew I wanted them gone. Whatever purpose they served was of no benefit to me.

I asked several doctors to remove them. They all declined stating that to remove them posed an unnecessary risk of surgery. They characterized the surgery as "non-therapeutic" and "unnecessary." According to the surgeons, the risk outweighed the benefit. I honestly couldn't claim that they caused me pain. So, they remained. I began to refer to them collectively as "it" or the "thing."

It was true. They caused no physical pain, but it opened the door to a flood of memories. What this piece of metal the size of a fingernail dredged up from my psyche were incredible memories of events from forty-years ago or more. There are memories there I did not want to revisit and prayed I never would.

Every man and woman that lives long enough will have a tragedy to endure. It's inevitable that someone we love will pass away too soon. Assorted disappointments befall us all. In my life, I refer to these occurrences collectively as "events."

Memories of some events are not dwelt upon and shouldn't be. They are put away. Tamped down in a dark corner of our mind and only to be revisited on rare occasions when the circumstances demand it. Otherwise, there is no room for such thoughts in a sane mind.

Eight weeks after my trip to the emergency room the nightmares resumed. My wife and I were wrong to assume that the events from our past would remain in our past. It went unsaid between us that the subject was a closed chapter. We had enjoyed a 40-year hiatus with only a couple nightmares as intense as these. The anomalous things they found in my leg awakened memories of real and horrific events. The scab of a partially healed wound was ripped off unexpectedly and raw nerves were exposed.

Back in 1977, my wife had encouraged me to begin a journal as a way of coping with the nightmares that haunted my sleep after the Devils Den incident. By recording everything, I managed to document the whole ugly mess of 1977. Once on paper I hoped the memories would drift away. I could let go of the compulsion to replay the events over and over in my mind. It was mostly successful.

With Sheila's patient support, I diligently recorded every nightmare following the 1977 incident. When events and circumstances caused these memories to bubble up and back into my conscious memory, journaling them helped to mitigate the terror. With support from my wife and diligence I filled an entire notebook in 1979 and began another.

After ten years of peace, a second event happened in 1987. It brought out the notebooks to be put into use once more. But only for a short while before being returned to storage. The event in 1987 was epic but brief.

This was 2012; I hoped that my wife had saved those notebooks. Painful as it may be to see them again, they could help me to cope. I knew the journaling process helped. I resumed writing almost immediately after the first 2013 nightmare. My wife flew to Michigan to open our storage locker and hunt for the notebooks. I was confident she could find them. It was worth every penny of airfare. From the bottom of a cedar chest she resurrected two blue spiral bound notebooks. One was a little more than half full. The other was full. She also found my sketchbook with drawings made from 1977 through 1979. I was stunned to see them again. My last journal entry was dated November 5, 1988. In dread of the consequences I would not read a single entry prior to that date for many months. I was afraid to review those memories because of the nightmares that accompany them. But it made no difference. All the nightmares came back in a flood of terror.

In March 2013, I went back online to take a second look at my medical records. I was surprised to discover the radiologist's report from October 25, 2012, was gone! In its place was a second report by a different radiologist dated November 7, 2012. The second report made no mention of the "artifacts" below my knee or the piece of metal above it. None of it was mentioned in this second report.

Instead, this report simply identified the Baker cyst and nothing more. The November 7, 2012 report failed to state that it was an amended or supplemental report. So, there was nothing to show a prior report ever existed. I was grateful that I secured copies of my x-rays before they too were edited or lost. Like a dolt, it was only then that it occurred to me: The Veterans Administration was an entity of the United States Government.

All through 2013 and 2014 the nightmares continued. I would wake up screaming and my wife would do her best to calm me. I did my best to document each dream before it evaporated.

My journal began to tell a story. I was amazed to find the dreams progressed chronologically. Like a made-for-TV movie, each dream dovetailed into the next. After a few weeks, I reviewed my prior journal entries and found what I had grown to suspect. I was reliving memories from the 1977 event.

Four Grinning Monkeys

Shadows from the hallway crept into my room,
long the monkeymen too I assume.
Never before in life had I seen, a form
that could grin, before I could scream.

A candle's flame dances before it grows dim,
one monkeyman's shadow had slowly crept in
on his knees and with ease, he is perched,
on the edge of my bed if you please.

The silence was broken one inch from my ear
as the monkeyman whispered "my boy I'm right here!"
Now monkeys were four and were masked to deceive
children, or even grown men if you please.

I started to tremble and covered my head,
but the monkeys, all four, crept close to my bed.
Outside of my covers four peeled with delight.
These monkeymen here, will take me this night?

Faces with grins approach me to say,
"Terry, won't you come with us and play?
Come with us now, give us your hand,
and we'll take you to an unbelievable land.

You may not remember the last time or when,
but come with us now and you'll see it again!
But I said I know you are not what you seem,
and if you are real, then why can't I scream?

This night the monkeymen take me with ease,
and I'm but a terrified child if you please.
These things are not men that are born on this earth,
near a star to the West is the place of their birth.

It matters not what I do, or I say,
tonight, like the others, they'll take me away.
Where shall we go and how long must I stay?
Tell me you four, tell me now I do pray.

We're going home Terry!
There's no reason for gloom.
See that star over there,
just east of your moon?

We traverse great distance, pick you up, and we're gone
to return you to bed before breaks the dawn.
We must take from you blood and things we do need,
many entities one day will be born of your seed.

When I'm taken away, can my mom hear my calls,
across all of space, through brick and through walls?

Will she think that I'm lost, or been seized from my bed?
Will she worry I suffer or fear I am dead?

She'll cry and sob while we go and play,
if I don't return before dawn brings the day.
And when I return will I come back whole,
or will sinister deeds take some terrible toll?

We'll soon arrive at the place we do dwell,
You'll see it neither is heaven nor hell,
a place with two suns light our days,
a place that is different but also the same.

The years have passed quickly as life slips from my grasp,
Pray tell me why did you hurt me I ask?
From earth you take away women and men
to tag us and track us toward what an end?

We are sentient beings that feel, self-aware.
But you are just monkeys and monkeys don't care.
As a child I had no voice to say
what may come to pass on some future day.

I have the need and right to know,
what was done to me so many years ago.
Surely you knew that one day I'd be grown,
no longer helpless, no longer alone.

Did you not believe that I'd live to confess?

The memories you stole and failed to suppress?

So flawed was your sinister plan ill conceived,

that others first scoff but then come to believe.

I swear by all that is holy and all that is right,

the next time you come to take me at night,

when four little monkeys crouch near my bed,

I'll take my revolver and shoot them all dead.

Lots of things are scary when you're eight years-old. This night I woke-up abruptly from a deep sleep in the comfort of my warm bed. Something was wrong. It was creepy. I could sense someone was in my room. It was that creepy feeling that I wasn't alone that woke me up. It's akin to the feeling you get when you realize a stranger is staring at you. I could feel eyes on me.

Two years earlier I had abandoned my night-light in favor of sleeping in a darkened bedroom. I regretted it now! Each nightmare I hoped to be my last. But then I'd have another.

This would be the fourth time in two weeks. Once more, I woke up from a deep sleep. I watched and listened hoping they wouldn't come. Wanting more sleep but afraid to shut my eyes. My eyes strained as I scanned the darkened room for movement or shadows.

Then from the corner of my eye I saw a shadow move by my closet door! As soon as I switched my gaze in its direction it would dart somewhere else or vanish. I continued to watch and listen. I could hear faint voices, but I couldn't make out the words at first.

This night I heard them before I saw them. Their words were faint and friendly at first, "Terry! Everything's okay! Won't you come and play with us?"

Out of the darkness stepped four little monkeys. They were grey and only about two feet tall with large yellow eyes. At first, they were kind of funny. All four wore the same broad grin. They had long arms and a tail. These were real monkeys and I was fully awake!

The one closest to me spoke, "Come with us and we'll have fun!"

I heard his words in my head, but the monkey's lips never moved. Their faces were all locked in the same eerie grin. It was as if they all wore identical masks. It felt like a standoff for a moment. I considered going with them at first. But where would they take me?

Did I go with them the last time? I couldn't remember. I was warned against going with strangers. These monkeys were familiar to me now. But they still frightened me.

Their grins grew less friendly. Rather than a grin, it turned into more of a scary smirk. I could sense they were growing impatient with me. Now the monkey faces were evil. I thought maybe they might jump on me and just take me away.

That was my real fear. I was afraid they were going to jump me and take me before I could scream for help. They might take me away from my home and I'd be lost forever in the place where children go when they vanish and are never found.

They inched closer until they formed a semi-circle around my bed with my back against my bookcase. The dim light from the window casts long tall shadows against the wall.

The monkeys continued to stare at me and smile. The closest one spoke again, "Come play with us. We'll have fun and we'll take you back home in just a little while." Like always, his lips never moved, he just grinned.

I realized these were not my friends and this wasn't right! Then, fully awake I screamed for my mother. I screamed so loud I woke up the whole household. When the hall light came on the monkeys vanished in a whirl of black shadows.

My dad came in and scooped me out of bed.

"What's wrong? More monkeys?" He was kind, but he was justifiably annoyed.

"Dad, you didn't see them. I was awake, and they were right here in my room again!"

He ignored my remark, "You can sleep with Mom and Dad again. But this is the last time. Okay buddy? We're going to leave a light on for you in the hallway and you will have to sleep in your own bed. You're too old for this. You're eight now. This has to stop."

I felt embarrassed. But fear overrode my shame. I slept with my parents for a fourth night in two weeks. That was something I hadn't done since I was five. I was eight-years old and didn't consider myself a little kid anymore. That night, I fell asleep between my parents feeling safe but still nervous, until I fell asleep.

I woke up to an empty bed. The school bus didn't run for another hour, so I didn't need to get up. On my way back from the bathroom I heard the word "monkeys." I knew I was being discussed. I quietly walked to the stairway and sat down on the top step to listen.

Over morning coffee, my sleep deprived parents sat at the kitchen table. The haze of Dad's cigarette smoke hung heavy in the air. They talked about my recent monkeymen nightmares that had rocked the whole household. My dad took his final sip of coffee. He had to leave in a minute to get to work on time. Their discussion had to wrap-up soon or he'd be late.

Grabbing his lunchbox, his parting comment to my mother was, "Something has to be done. Let's leave the hall light on for a while. When I carried him into our bedroom last night, he was shaking and crying again."

Wringing her hands like she always did when worried, she said, "I know. It took a long time for him to settle down."

He asked my mom as if she would know the answer, "Why monkeys?"

Mom just shrugged her shoulders.

"Of all the things that scare him, of all the monsters he's met in past nightmares, why monkeys? I need to get a good night's sleep to work. This has got to stop ... he woke both the girls too," my dad said. I felt terrible that I woke the entire family.

Mom said, "I'll think about it … and I'll talk to him again. Who knows, maybe it will just stop on its own with the hall light on?"

"I hope so. I'll think about it too. We can come up with something. Try talking to him again. See if he'll open-up to you and tell you about these nightmares," Dad replied on his way out the door.

With a peck on the cheek, she assured him she would talk to me. I went back to my own bed, but not back to sleep.

After breakfast my mother got my two sisters off to school. She held me back that day. I knew what she was going to ask.

My mom began, "Honey, I want to talk to you for a minute before you go to school. I'll drive you, so you won't be late."

Apologetically I began, "Mom, I'm sorry about last night. It just scared me so bad!"

She said, "Terry, I need you to tell me about these nightmares, so your dad and I can help you. What do these monkeys do that scares you?"

"Mom, they want me to come with them! Like I told you before, there are four of them and they're all wearing a mask. They all wear the same mask too," I said, trying to explain something so bizarre with the limited vocabulary of an eight-year-old.

She pleaded, "Help me understand. Are you afraid of all monkeys, like the ones at the zoo or monkeys on the TV?"

"No Mom, it's just these four same monkeys that come in my room. They look like real monkeys, but not like on TV. These are the monkeymen. The monkeymen scare me! They want me to go with them. Sometimes I think I'll go. Sometimes I even think I went with them before," I said.

My mother pressed on, "But you know monkeys can't hurt you! Have you tried telling them to go away? You just tell them you don't want to play with them anymore! You can do that. You can tell them to leave you alone and order them to get out. You can do that!"

"Okay Momma. I'll try. I'll tell them to get out of my room and leave me alone! I'm afraid they might take me away with them and I might not be able to come home!" I was crying now.

"Honey I … I don't know. You just must try. We'll leave the hall light on at night now. But you can't sleep with Mom and Dad anymore. It's not fair to wake up your sisters by screaming either. If you think these monkeymen are real and not just bad dreams, then where do they go when the lights come on?" Mom asked.

"Mom, I don't know where they come from and I don't know where they go when the light comes on either. I don't think I'm asleep when the monkeymen come." I couldn't grasp it myself. Trying to communicate it to my mother was impossible.

"See! You might think you're awake. It can feel like you're awake but it's all a dream. These are just bad dreams," she said with confidence.

"But Mom, I'm awake! I'm not asleep! I wake up and the monkeymen are sneaking into my bedroom. They just step out of the dark and stare at me. I see their shadows move across my wall first," I said, hoping to make her understand.

My mother was running out of patience, "Tell Momma what else do these monkeys do? They just stare at you?"

I said, "Yeah Mom, they smile and they're nice. They tell me they're my friends and they want to play. They want me to go with them and play someplace else. Then I get afraid because they start to look mean suddenly. I'm afraid they're going to take me away."

"Honey, it's okay. We'll figure this out! I bet we can find a way to monkey-proof your room and keep them away! You just have to trust Mom and Dad, okay," she said with a hug.

With that she wiped away the tears and I was off to school.

When I came home that evening, everything seemed normal. After dinner, Mom and Dad ushered me into my bedroom and shut the door. Dad was holding a half-inch roll of weather stripping. I was very confused.

Bending down on one knee to be at eye-level, my dad confidently assured me, "Son, I can fix the problem of monkeys getting into your room at night! I bought some special tape that's guaranteed to do the trick!"

I asked, "You really can Dad?"

I was astounded. If they make special tape to keep them away, then that means these aren't nightmares at all! They must be real if they make tape to keep them out! I had been right all along! But I was still skeptical.

"Yes, I have a special tape they use for these things," my dad said, whistling softly as he went about his work.

I was unconvinced that black squishy tape could keep the monkeymen away. Some part of me knew real monkeys were only in the jungle or at the zoo, but something was in my room. These are so real, and Dad just confirmed it for me! But, if they're real, that makes them extra scary too.

He finished in just a few minutes. With confidence he assured me, "This will keep you safe all night long!"

Dad was smiling. My mom seemed thrilled too. But I was still processing it all. If the monkeymen are real, then where do they come from? My mind raced with questions.

Dad said, "Okay son, you're safe from monkeys and monkeymen. You can sleep with your light on too. Just until you're feeling safe again. Isn't that better than leaving on the hall light?"

"Thanks Dad, thanks Mom!"

It seemed incredible. No more visits from the monkeymen and they can't take me away! I was overjoyed. I wanted to believe. My dad had never lied to me before. A couple yards of special tape did the trick! The monkeymen were gone!

Eight weeks passed and not a single monkey. I never again had a visit from the monkeymen! I had one or two more dreams *about* the monkeymen. But those were different, I knew those were only nightmares. The monkeymen were real. Another six weeks went by and now it was May. Maybe the monkeymen really were just dreams? I doubted it, because the tape worked.

The weather was warm now and summer vacation was just around the corner. I was outside on a beautiful Saturday. This would be a day I'd remember for a lifetime. It was cloudless with a spring breeze and an occasional wind gust. Good kite weather. The windows in the house were open. My mother was at home watching her soaps and never more than 60-feet away. There was nothing wrong with her hearing. I don't recall neighbors around.

I was in the backyard shooting arrows into a block of hay. I was proud! This was an adult bow and arrow set for target shooting. Looking back, I'd never give one of my children such a lethal weapon when they were eight. It really was a different time, in so many ways, back then.

While I was loading an arrow's notch onto my bowstring I saw a dark shadow move across the grass under my feet. I assumed it was a cloud. But the shadow made a perfect circle. I looked up.

There was a large silver disc-shaped object directly over my head. I was dumbstruck. My eyes tried to take in all the details. My mind raced through everything I knew about things that could fly. What could this be? Could it hurt me?

Airplanes and helicopters, I immediately dismissed. The only thing left on my mental checklist was perhaps a balloon or dirigible of some sort.

But balloons are not made of aluminum and dirigibles aren't round. Balloons don't sit perfectly still in the spring breeze. Whatever this was, it was something I'd never seen before. I was overwhelmed! It was exciting too!

This thing made no noise and wobbled slightly in the breeze. I'd estimate it was no more than 50 feet over my head. For some odd reason I felt compelled to put down my bow and lie down on the freshly mowed lawn and stare up at the thing for a better view. In hindsight of course, that made no sense. But that's what I did, and that puzzles me to this day.

This thing was amazingly beautiful. It was shiny and gorgeous in the way a brand-new sports car is gorgeous. I called the body silver at the time. It could have been highly polished aluminum or God-knows what.

Its edges curled upward. But otherwise it was perfectly flat like a pancake. I remember being sorely disappointed I couldn't see the top of it. I wanted to see if there were windows.

On the bottom, there were no openings or doorways of any kind. No seams or rivets. There wasn't an exhaust pipe. There was nothing printed on it. I expected to see USAF or even CCCP painted on the bottom. There were no insignias or numbers. The bottom was one seamless piece of shiny metal.

Having assembled more than a few plastic model airplanes, I had a vague idea of how mechanical things were put together. I thought there should be rivets or seams visible. Whatever this was, it had to have been put together.

I wished there were windows, so I could see who was driving. There could be a dome or something sitting on the top. Where do the wheels come down if it wants to land? My mind continued racing.

This is anecdotal but there was an odd static electric charge in the air. I felt the fine hairs on my forearms stand up. I could smell the freshly mowed grass and ionized air. It was the scent of fresh air after a thunderstorm mixed with the sweet smell of the freshly mowed lawn. There was a change in the acoustics as well. I remember that the whole neighborhood was silent! There were no cars or TVs blaring from open windows. There was nothing. I laid flat on my back looking up with a mixture of fear and amazement. This was something new.

It was broad daylight in a neighborhood usually full of children. Surely dozens of people were staring at this thing just like me at that very minute! I laid there for what felt like 10 minutes. The passage of time is difficult for a child to estimate. Especially under such bizarre circumstances. I have no idea how much time passed. I'm certain it was no more than thirty minutes, but it could have been as few as ten.

The saucer wobbled and tilted upward at about a 30-degree angle toward the back of the house, so it'd clear the power lines. Then it silently shot off. Traveling from a dead stop to the speed of a bullet. It was out of sight in a second.

I had no way to estimate its speed, but it was fast. It was very fast. It traveled fast enough to have been missed in the blink of an eye. To this day, I wonder why I didn't yell for my mother when I first saw it. If she had seen it too, that would have avoided so many problems.

As soon as it was gone, I jumped to my feet and screamed, "Mom!" I stood there like a statue. My eyes were fixed on the hole in the sky where it had vanished.

My poor mother thought I had hurt myself or, worse yet, had killed a neighbor with an arrow to the head. Other than yelling once for my mother I don't remember screaming. But I guess I did. I must have. My throat felt raw like it feels after I yell.

My mother came running. After a quick assessment for blood she shifted her focus to stop my screaming. Grabbing me by both shoulders she shook me violently saying, "Stop it! You will stop hollering this instant. My God! The neighbors will think you've lost your mind! What is wrong with you?"

My mother was always cognizant of what the neighbors might think. To her defense it was true. Our neighbors were always on the lookout for grist to feed the gossip mill. At some point I must have stopped screaming.

In a whisper she calmly said, "Now let's get you inside and make sure you're alright." Pulling me by the arm she dragged me into our kitchen. My eyes were fixed on the sky until we entered the house.

Once inside, the words came pouring out. I asked, "Did you see it, did you see it Mom? I was afraid because it was so big and so close! I thought they might take me away or something! What was it? Was it a spaceship? What was it?"

I thought, my mom's a grown up. She'll have the answer. She'll be able to explain it to me. We sat down at the kitchen table.

"Terry, what you saw was probably a jet. You know what jets are. It could have been something secret the army made. I don't know what you saw but I know for sure you did not see a flying saucer," Mom assured me.

I'd seen flying saucers on television shows like: *The Outer Limits, Twilight Zone, My Favorite Martian* and others. Comic books galore featured stories about visitors from outer space with laser beams laying waste to buildings. But I knew those weren't real.

"But Mom! It looked just like the ones on TV!" My mother knew I didn't lie. Besides, she wasn't there! How could she possibly know what I saw?

At that moment my two older sisters came bounding in. Sensing blood in the water they demanded to know more. Of course, my mom offered up, "Oh, Terry thinks he saw a spaceship in the backyard and he threw a fit!"

They pulled up chairs eager to hear the whole story.

My eldest sister began with sarcasm. She asked, "Was it a real spaceship? Did the monkeys fly it? Did the monkeymen come out to get you?" Then came the fits of laughter.

My mother gave my sisters both a warning, "Now don't you go and tease him!"

She was well intentioned, but the damage was done, and a lesson was learned.

Then she promptly gave them every detail. They now had the ammunition needed to make my life hell for weeks. The abuse began without delay.

I was one pissed-off eight-year-old. Why wouldn't they believe me? No one could tell me what I saw because they weren't there! My mother tried to calm me down and explain it all away as something other than a flying saucer. I wondered why?

She was certain I had seen an airplane. Probably a jet of some kind. Of course, she didn't believe in flying saucers and such things. She certainly didn't want her son to tell stories that reflected badly on the family.

Mom had one idea left. She asked me to draw a picture of exactly what I saw. Handing me a felt-tip pen and a piece of construction paper she sat next to me at the kitchen table. At the age of eight, I was a decent artist. I took a few moments to think about it. It didn't take me more than a minute to complete.

I drew a circle. Anything I drew in two dimensions couldn't convey the three-dimensional image I saw. Plus, it wasn't just the round thing in the sky. There was the ionized air, the smell of the grass, silence and the hair on my arms standing up. It was a sensation greater than the visual sighting of a flying saucer. It was more than just witnessing something. It was a real experience.

If you've ever seen a UFO up-close, you understand. There's nothing else like it. No hoax could recreate the ionized air or the mixture of awe and fear. Seeing a flying disc shoot across the sky is one thing. Seeing one stopped directly over your head is an entirely different matter.

Because I was so upset, my mother called a handful of neighbors and asked if anyone saw, "something strange in the sky?"

The inevitable reply was of course, "Why no Anne. Why do you ask?"

Without realizing the repercussion from my peers in the neighborhood, my mother told them all, "Oh, Terry thinks he saw a spaceship and now he's throwing a fit."

By 6:00 PM I had neighbor kids on me like a cheap suit. I'm just grateful that summer vacation was right around the corner. Soon everyone would have other amusements like summer camp and the swimming pool at the park. But for now, I was the target of opportunity.

My father got home from work and was intercepted by my mom before he took off his cap. My poor dad. When he got home at the end of his day he was tired and dirty. All he wanted was a warm bath and a hot meal. Many times, I heard my dad plead with my mom, "Unless someone died, can't it just wait until after dinner?"

Her interception was successful, and Dad was diverted into their bedroom. I could hear muffled voices but at least no one was yelling. He came out and promptly escorted me into my bedroom and closed the door. That was worrisome.

Dad said, "Alright son, what happened today?" Looking unhappy he asked, "What's all this nonsense about seeing flying saucers in the backyard?"

"No Dad. There was just one flying saucer and it was..." I said, trying to be clear. But I could sense it was time to squelch my excitement by his facial expression and the tone of voice.

He was irritated with my answer. I told him the truth. Before I was half-done he rolled his eyes. I could see he was getting mad. The madder he got, the faster I spoke. I hoped to convey enough information to validate my experience before he exploded. Sadly, I was unsuccessful.

He said, "Now son, we've already discussed this whole thing, didn't we? Don't you remember just back in March? When we talked about the monkeys? I told you they weren't real? Remember?"

"But Dad if the monkeymen weren't real then why did you use the special tape to keep them out? How come it worked? You wouldn't need tape if they were just bad dreams." I said.

Now he looked confused. Neither of us spoke for an awkward minute or two.

"Remember Dad, you said you could keep the monkeymen out? You said they make special tape that keeps away monkeys and monkeymen. But it's just tape for the windows."

I knew my dad had lied to me. There was no magic tape like he said. I found the bag in the garage. It was weather stripping to keep out the cold. I was eight, but I wasn't stupid.

Dad clearly wasn't prepared for that. I was surprised that he kept his composure.

"Terry, it worked because you believed it works that's all! It made the monkeys go away didn't it? Remember when we talked about monsters, ghosts, and flying saucers? Remember that?" Dad said.

I was pleading now, "Yeah, but Dad, you said there were no flying saucers. But I saw one."

My dad and I had talked about flying saucers once before. There was a story about someone who saw a flying saucer on the nightly news. The news reported on a couple who saw a flying saucer in their backyard. They even let them tell all about it on the news. I remembered Dad said it was all, "outer space bullshit made up by the Russians to scare us." It sure scared me.

Dad said, "Terry, I told you that ghosts, monsters, and flying saucers aren't real. Godzilla was just a man. He was just a guy in a rubber monster suit, remember? Stomping on toy busses and making those weird sounds. Remember when we talked about the satellite, Sputnik?"

"Yeah Dad, you told me everything in the sky is made right here on earth. Put together in a factory by people."

"Right! You know I wouldn't tell you something that's not true!" he added.

But I wasn't sure I could trust him to tell me the truth now.

"Son, you can't walk around the neighborhood and tell people you saw a flying saucer! They'll think something's wrong with you... or with us. Understand?"

"Yes sir." I could tell my dad had reached his limit. Next, he would yell at me, and I didn't like being yelled at. He scared me when he yelled. It made me cry.

"Well then, let's agree that whatever you saw, it was a shiny jet! Okay? Then we can have some supper and stop all this nonsense! Everything will be okay. Now son, tell me what you saw," he said leaning back with his arms folded.

I did the unthinkable. I lied. After a pause, I swallowed hard and said, "Well... it could have been a jet."

"There, you see how these things are! Sometimes we can't believe our eyes. It's like the monkeys. It's all over and done with. Now we can put this whole thing to bed," Dad said obviously pleased.

Those would turn out to be a poor choice of words. The flying saucer matter wasn't put to bed. Our lies hadn't changed reality. What I saw was not a jet. What I saw was a real flying saucer.

The consequences began a week later with a new round of horrific nightmares. These always began with lights in the sky and shadowy people lurking around the house at night. Then they would take a more sinister turn.

Shadowy figures soon grab me, and I'm carried away by many hands. It was the worst kind of nightmare. It's what made the four monkeymen so scary. I was taken away and held down by man-sized bugs that hurt me. Intelligent six-foot-tall praying mantis-like beings who ignored my pleas. It was impossible to abort the dream once the shadowy figures appeared. The dream had to run its entire course before I could scream.

Oddly, I never had a single dream about flying saucers. Not one time. These were not the usual boogey-man under the bed dreams that all kids have now and again. These were incredibly ugly dreams. These always had the same big bug thing with the head of a praying mantis.

No way seeing the flying saucer caused this new round of nightmares! My parents and the whole family believed these new nightmares were centered on flying saucers. No one was listening.

They were wrong, and they had never been centered on flying saucers. I had trouble making them understand they weren't connected just because the nightmares started after I saw the flying saucer in the backyard.

Besides, how could the two have been connected? The flying saucer was so cool! I saw a real flying saucer and it didn't hurt me! I wanted to know who they were and where they came from. Many afternoons I searched the empty sky and wondered where they went.

My dad's story that everything in the sky was made by men on earth wasn't true. This thing came from another planet! There must be real spacemen too! If they ever came back I wouldn't scream for my mother again.

As a child I fantasized about talking to the spacemen. I could help them! I could go to Washington as their ambassador. They could use me to communicate great things like a cure for cancer! I imagined banner headlines, "Terry Works with Spacemen and Saves the World!"

A decade later I'd meet a real spaceman. It would be, "up close and personal" as the saying goes. Nothing in my childhood fantasies or my worst nightmare could come close to what I saw and experienced. There would be no ambassadorship in my future. No cure for cancer. No dialogue whatsoever. Only pain and terror.

But seeing a flying saucer was fun! I felt special. I felt like they chose me to see them. I just knew they were friendly. They had to be good!

I dealt with the teasing as well as any eight-year-old. My schoolmates dropped the whole matter in a week, moving on to new victims to torment.

But my sisters would not let it go. Their teasing continued, and they upped the ante by scaring the wits out of me. Popping up unexpectedly from behind a table or waiting for me around a corner. Then they'd jump out and walk around robotically screaming, "Must get Terry!" To this day I don't like to be surprised.

But that would all abruptly end when I retaliated. Two could dish out torment. I had a plan.

One night I hid under the living room sofa. I waited patiently for what felt like an hour. I was waiting for the opportunity I knew would come any minute now. Wait for it!

My eldest sister Judy sat down on the sofa with her "princess phone" on her lap. It was her usual weeknight routine. After dinner cleanup she'd sit on the couch and chat with her girlfriend on the phone. She'd talk until she was forced to surrender the living room and the TV to my father.

I knew she was totally unaware of my presence. She began her nightly chat as only teenage girls can. Still I waited.

When I was sure she was fully engaged in her conversation. I reached out from underneath the sofa grabbed her by both ankles and let out a scream that would wake the dead!

My sister wet her pants … and the sofa. She ran for the bathroom and I ran for my bedroom.

This got our father involved. He sat me down for a stern, "talking to." In his voice reserved for the harshest of reprimands he demanded to know, "Now what makes you think you have the right to scare your sister like that? Huh? Huh!"

This was the point in the conversation where I would historically act contrite and promise, "Dad I'm sorry. It will never happen again I swear it!"

No way. Not this time. "I want them to know what it feels like to be scared. If they don't want more of the same, you better tell them to stop teasing me." Because I felt I was on a roll I added, "Spank me if you want to but you better make them stop it or else!"

Dad was stunned! I stared him down and refused to apologize or even speak. This was not our usual father to son talk. This was an adult conversation. This was no longer the same eight-year-old boy. I had changed. I refused be intimidated and lied to again.

It is sad to note that following this incident our relationship would never be as close. Some bit of that father-son closeness a little boy has for his dad was gone. He'd lied to me about the "monkey tape." I'd always been told the truth was a valuable thing.

My father softened his tone, "I'll speak with them, they won't tease you anymore. Is there anything you want Dad to know? You can always talk to Dad."

"Nope that's it. Thank you, Dad."

My sisters never teased me again. Years later they both told me there was a marked change in my behavior shortly after I saw the flying saucer. I started to avoid being outside after dark. When the streetlights came on, I would run for the safety of home.

They noticed other things. We had a neighbor. She was a very kind Asian woman we all called, Sue. She had an amazing flower garden and would bake delicious things for us. I'd known her all my life but now her appearance made me nervous and I began avoiding her.

I had a new fear of being out in open spaces. This was something new too. I felt threatened by something, but I couldn't pinpoint what made me feel uncomfortable.

Since seeing the flying saucer in my backyard, my belief system had changed radically. I learned that grown-ups don't know all the answers and they don't always tell the truth.

There was something else in the universe. Out in all the stars in the night sky. But grown-ups refused to discuss it. Whenever the subject came up, my dad's commentary was always the same, "That's all bullshit!" Or, "the Russians are behind it all!"

Adults wouldn't listen to me. But I knew something. It was something big too. They were probably jealous that they hadn't been chosen to see them.

Children need to feel secure and be able to trust their parents to protect them. I didn't believe they could keep me from monkeymen. Weather stripping tape be damned. I was vulnerable, and I knew it. Aside from the insecurity, what hurt the most was that they refused to believe me. I wasn't a liar. They were the ones who lied.

Nighttime became unfriendly now. I wasn't sleeping well. My grades slipped most probably due to lack of sleep. I'd wake around 2:00

AM and be unable to get back to sleep. Some nights I simply couldn't get to sleep at all. I began to dread bedtime.

After a few months, my dad decided I needed to see the family doctor. Who would, "Put this flying saucer business to rest once and for all." He thought a doctor could fix my behavior like curing chicken pox or measles.

My dad wanted an end to what he called, "the spaceship bullshit" that was interfering with his ability to get a good night's sleep. He was tired of the disruption to our usual household harmony too. He just wanted things back the way they were before that spring day in May of 1963 and back before the monkeymen.

Without warning, my dad picked me up from school an hour early one day. I was hustled off to the doctor's office. Dad said, "We're going to have a little talk with the doctor and get you checked over."

I knew the subject.

I realized on the drive over that I had a newfound fear of the doctor too! For that matter anyone in a lab coat made me uncomfortable. This was my first visit to the doctor since the incident months earlier. I had never been afraid of the doctor before. This time it felt different.

We arrived, and my dad had a long discussion with the doctor. They were out of my earshot of course. After a few minutes the doctor nodded his head and turned his attention to me.

I was reluctant to get on the examination table. I had never given the exam room a second thought but now it made me fearful. I was especially anxious of the overhead examination light for some reason and I could feel my heart pounding in my chest.

The doctor sensed my anxiety.

He said, "Don't worry, no shot today. I'm just going to look you over a bit."

He gave me the usual, "Stick out your tongue." He pressed on my abdomen. I doubted there was any real medical examination going on here. I had become distrustful of adults.

Then he casually said, "So, your dad said you saw something in the sky in the backyard. What was it?"

I played innocent. "What do you mean," I asked?

"Dad tells me you saw something in the sky in your backyard. He said it scared you and now you're having dreams about flying saucers."

"Yeah, I saw something. I have nightmares too. But not about flying saucers."

In a sincere voice he said, "You're not in trouble son. Tell me what you saw. Tell me all about your bad dreams about these flying saucers."

"It was a jet," I said.

"Now, why would a jet give you bad dreams about spaceships?" He crossed his arms and frowned.

"It just gave me bad dreams. I don't know why. I guess it could have been a jet." I felt myself tearing up. I was livid! But I tried not to cry.

Satisfied with my answer, he said, "Now we're getting somewhere! Okay, what did this jet look like?"

"Well, it was silver, and … it was in the sky, but that's all!"

"Well, I'm going to ask Dad to leave the room and then we can talk, okay?"

My dad picked up the cue and left the exam room.

He began, "Now, you can trust me boy. I'm your doctor. I want you to be well. You need to be a man now and tell me everything you saw that day. Man, to man."

I thought about it for a while. Honestly, I wanted to tell someone who'd believe me. Against my better judgment I decided to trust him. I told him the true story. It was more like I spewed out the story. It came out of me in a torrent. It felt good to get it all out.

He listened and occasionally nodded, but he never changed his facial expression to betray what he really thought.

Once I'd finished, he asked my dad to come back into the examination room. "What kind of TV shows is he watching?"

They had a discussion. They spoke as if I wasn't even in the room! I was baffled. Why would the doctor want to know what cartoons I watched?

The doctor explained his diagnosis, "The problem here is an overactive imagination made worse by the influence of Space Ghost and Johnny Quest cartoons." He then shifted his focus back to me. "Boy, when you're eight-years old ..."

I corrected him, "I'm nine. I'm nine-years old now!"

"When you're nine, your mind can play tricks on you. I'm sure you think you saw a flying saucer but you and I both know things like that don't really exist. Don't we?"

He waited for my reply.

I wanted to hit him. Several uneasy seconds ticked by before I said in a whisper, "Yes sir."

The doctor looked toward my dad for acknowledgement. "That's right, we know that those things only exist in comic books and television programs. Maybe in your imagination too? Like make-believe, right boy?"

Even at nine-years old I knew a leading question when I heard one. I was boxed. I could only respond with a "yes" or a "no."

"Yes sir." I felt defeated.

While I sat on the exam table the doctor wheeled his stool over next to me. My dad pulled up a chair next to him. The doctor then took on a stern affect.

"Now, repeat after me boy. There are no flying saucers and nothing from the sky can hurt me. Now go ahead and say it. Say it loud so Dad can hear you too."

"There are no flying saucers, and nothing can hurt me," that's as far as I got. I welled up with tears. But I never actually cried. I was furious. I accepted that nine-year-old boys had no power.

"I've advised Dad to make sure you watch healthier things on television. Better yet, get outside and play some ball or ride your bike."

"Yes sir." I thought, yeah, yeah. I'd heard all that crap before.

I'm sure to help justify his fee the doctor turned back to my dad and said, "Well, it's all over now. I predict one or two more nightmares and that will be the end of it. No more nightmares and no more spaceships."

Obviously pleased with himself, the doctor turned to my dad and they shook hands. We headed for the car.

I don't remember most of the ride home. Of course, we had to get an ice cream cone on our way. Rocky Road is the price of a nine-year-old's dignity.

My parents' idea of healthier television was Three Stooges reruns. Later, my taste would switch to Perry Mason. But for now, it was non-stop Moe, Larry, and Shemp or Curley depending on the episode. Slapstick's funny when you're nine. But only for so long.

Pretty quickly, Moe and Larry were on everyone's last nerve. My TV restrictions were all but lifted after a few weeks of the Stooges.

As for the neighborhood gossip mill, there's always new gossip. I became yesterday's news in a week or two. Talk in the neighborhood switched from Terry's UFO to teen pregnancies, extramarital affairs, and the like.

It took an entire year, but eventually the nightmares died down. No thanks to the doctor who betrayed my trust. I still needed the nightlight and didn't care to be outside at night. Especially not out in the open.

A few uneventful years had passed. I'm sure that we all took it for granted that life had returned to normal. I was eleven-years old now. It was 1966.

It was January and it was bitterly cold outside. The temperature was probably in the teens with ice and an inch or so of blowing snow. Dinner was over, and I finished my homework in short order. I had just enough time to watch a little TV before bedtime. I don't recall what I watched but it wasn't anything spooky. It had been an ordinary day in all regards.

About 9:00 PM bedtime was officially announced. I went upstairs to brush my teeth and do the whole bedtime ritual. Shortly afterward I climbed into my bed and my mother tucked me in. The bed felt warm and cozy. I could hear the cold wind outside and felt glad to be somewhere warm. I had no difficulty getting to sleep that evening.

When I opened my eyes, I found I was sitting upright in my bed! It was the middle of the night. Brilliant multicolored lights were shining through the heavy drapes and blinds that covered my window.

The lights were brighter than any morning sunrise. Green and yellow lit up my bedroom like a baseball stadium at a night game. The light cast long shadows behind everything in the room.

These weren't automobile headlights. They were not emergency lights from a fire truck or a police car. All the Christmas lights were stowed away for another season. But at the time I didn't give it much thought! How could I be disinterested?

There was that odd noise too. It was the kind of noise made by very large machines. A pulsing mechanical hum at a steady volume. It wasn't so much loud as it was powerful. I could feel it in my chest like a bass guitar note on a giant amplifier. My bed quivered. The vibration caused the plastic airplanes on my desk to dance. One, close to the edge, fell off and onto the floor.

Neither the hum nor the lights varied in intensity. They were constant, so whatever was out there it wasn't just passing by.

I sat and watched it while sitting in my bed. I knew the hum and lights were coming from outside my bedroom window. I felt oddly disinterested about what was going on. I'd characterize my mood as curiously apathetic.

Usually I'd call out for my mom. But I didn't even consider it this time. I remembered when happened when I told mom when I was eight. Besides, there was no need to wake up the household. I was content to just watch for a while.

Despite my disinterest, I felt compelled to look out the window and see whatever was out there. I don't know what I expected to see but I wasn't afraid. I swung my legs over the side of the bed. My feet hit the floor and I walked to the window. I pulled back the drapes and peeked through the blinds. Just outside my second story, bedroom window was the source of the lights and the hum.

It was a flying saucer. It was shrouded in a heavy fog that rose from underneath somewhere. There it was! It was hovering over the front lawn just a few feet outside my bedroom window.

It looked like the one I saw in 1963. Except this time, I could see the top! There was a dome on top just like I expected. That was the source of the lights and the hum! My only emotion was satisfaction that I finally got a peek of the topside! But that enthusiasm faded quickly as apathy overtook the excitement again.

I had pulled the drapes back and I tucked a corner into the venetian blinds. It gave me a hands-free unobstructed view. The lights were intense enough to hurt my eyes. It was hard to stare at it for more than a few seconds. It was like trying to look at the sun.

I never felt the slightest bit of fear! With the compulsion to see satisfied, I felt content. I simply had no opinion or interest whatsoever.

I turned around and walked back to my bed while this thing sat outside my bedroom window. Glancing back, I made a mental note of the curtains stuck in the blinds and my model airplane on the floor. I pulled the covers up and fell back to sleep immediately.

The morning was a weird experience too. It was as if I had just laid down, blinked, and it was dawn! It was as if no time had passed between shutting my eyes and opening them. It was like I had blinked.

I had no dreams. As soon as my eyes opened it was morning and I was fully awake and alert.

A Vought F4U-4 fighter plane lay upside down on the floor. At first, I was puzzled. Now how did that happen? I could have stepped on it!

Then I remembered. The hum had vibrated my model airplane off my desk and onto the carpeting. There it lay! Upside down on the floor! I was excited!

I immediately turned my attention to the window. The curtain was tucked neatly between the venetian blinds! Just like I'd left it! It was confirmation that what happened that evening really did happen. It was no dream.

I had no way to know for sure it had left. But if it were still outside, there'd be a lot of commotion! The household was alive with the usual morning chaos of children preparing for school. No louder than usual.

This was my second sighting! I was a participant in so much as a passive observer can be a participant. This saucer was as real as the one I saw in my backyard three years earlier. Perhaps it was even the same flying saucer?

I was puzzled by my disinterest during the whole thing? The lights and the hum replayed in my mind. Now I had proof that this wasn't a dream. It was all the validation I needed. Now, I felt on top of the world!

The one I saw three years earlier could have just been lost. It could have taken a wrong turn at Albuquerque, like they said in the cartoon, and just ended-up in my backyard by happenstance! But now a second flying saucer was parked outside my window! This was no mistake. They were visiting me!

I understood the difference between an accident and an, "on-purpose." This thing purposefully visited me. I was thrilled. I had no idea the role I played in this whole affair, but I was a part of something big!

I sat back on my bed smiling. My doctor, the man who violated my trust and made me lie three years earlier … I searched my limited vocabulary for just the right name to call him. The best word I could come up with was, "asshole." I wanted so badly to tell him, "Doctor, spaceships are real. And you sir! You are an asshole!"

As to who piloted that spaceship back in 1963? It crossed my mind on occasion, but I never dwelt on it. After this encounter, I knew for certain that flying saucers were real. I knew that both encounters really happened. With those issues settled, my curiosity turned to who was flying these things.

I tried to follow this matter to a logical conclusion. If UFOs were made in the USA, why visit me? Why twice? If these flying saucers were made by the Russians, we would have surely shot them down. Everyone knew our air force was superior.

So, if the Russians didn't make flying saucers and they weren't from our air force, who else on this planet could make flying saucers? No one! They must come from another planet!

If the spaceships are real, that means there must be real spacemen inside to fly them! Living beings had to build the spaceship somewhere. There had to be a spaceship factory on a faraway planet. There had to be mechanics too! Guys to maintain them and fix them when they break down.

When they finished their work at the end of the day they had to have a home to go to! They probably had wives who cooked dinner like Mom. There must be grocery stores, farmers, children, and schools. This was an epiphany. It added up to an entire civilization somewhere else in the sky. It was an incredibly large concept for an eleven-year-old boy.

If the flying saucers came from outer space, they had to come from Mars or Venus. I had no evidence to base that on except for my rudimentary study of the earth and planets in elementary school.

I had never thought this far before. I knew. Now I was sure that spaceships and space people were real. I knew they came from a civilization in outer space with factories and houses! I dressed for school and did my best to hide my newfound exuberance. I had an entirely fresh topic for my daydreams in arithmetic class.

At breakfast I nonchalantly asked, "Did anyone see those lights last night? It had to have been a fire truck, right?"

"Nope."

"Never saw a thing."

"Slept right through it."

"Un-uh," my sister muttered with her mouthful of breakfast cereal.

I was happy to know that what I saw three years ago was real too. My curtains and the model airplane on the floor were my proof. But I still didn't want to think about monkeymen.

My elation was short lived. With the return of the flying saucer came the return of the nightmares. The stranger-in-my-room nightmares returned with a vengeance. So, did the nightmare images of big insect-like things manipulating tools with long, thin fingers. My fear of being out in open spaces returned too. Scary as hell. But they were brief this time. A couple months passed, and the nightmares became fewer and fewer. By the end of the school year they were gone again.

I never spoke about my 1963 incident to another living soul. Nor did I ever discuss the lights outside my window when I was eleven. The incidents in 1963 and 1966 proved to be but a taste of what was coming. Still, I felt smug in my knowledge. I knew something other people didn't believe and wouldn't believe. I filed it away with other childhood memories that were important.

These were very big issues for a little boy to process without assistance. So, I did my best. I reasoned that UFOs must be here to study us. Maybe they've been watching us for thousands of years, periodically checking in to gage our progress. Maybe even assisting with our progress? They could have been manipulating our bodies for thousands of years and accelerating our progress. These are friendly, "space brothers" here to help us out. Kind of like super heroes, I concluded. Except they were real.

Aside from fantasy daydreams in math class, I went on with my life. As the nightmares ebbed, my thoughts turned to other things. Following the 1963 incident, I learned that no one wanted to hear about flying saucers. I saw how people who said they saw a UFO were treated, like they were telling stories. I was told so often that what I saw was not a flying saucer, that at times even I questioned what I saw. My life would have been much easier if they had just been a bad dream. But they were real.

Life went on. Ten years. Ten glorious years and a mostly normal adolescence. A whole decade with nothing but an occasional nightmare. The pictures that were once in vivid color had faded around the edges. They were still there but more like aged photographs from the shoebox.

Strangely, it was the scent of the grass from back in 1963 that stayed the strongest. That never faded, not even to this day. If I had to pick which of our five senses made for the sharpest memories, I'd have chosen things we see. Our visual images. But the fragrance of that freshly mowed grass takes me back there every time.

A Close Call

It was the Christmas season 1987. Extraterrestrial beings and flying saucers were the furthest thing from my mind. Those experiences were real. The memories were real too but locked away in a vault in my mind. In a place I very rarely visited.

My first two sightings happened when I was eight and eleven-years old, respectively. I saw two flying saucers. Two silver disc shaped objects that could have been identical. That was back when I was a child and I viewed the world like a child.

Most people live their entire life without ever seeing a UFO. But I saw two before my twelfth birthday! I reminded myself of that fact from time-to-time. I felt proud.

That was a long time ago. Back when extraterrestrial beings were still my space brothers. During my third encounter I learned the truth.

They come here from places outside of our solar system, and they are not our space brothers. I felt fortunate to have survived the 1977 event and all that followed it. Sadly, the third encounter would cost my best friend his career and marriage. A few short years later it took his life.

But that was ten years ago. In 1987 I was married with a couple kids and all was well. I was working too hard but otherwise life was good. Except for a rare nightmare, my life was wonderful. Flying saucers were a closed chapter in my life. Done and over with. The whole UFO topic never made my reading list. I preferred history and non-fiction genres.

We were Christmas shopping. Not my favorite pastime, but having children changes things. Buying toys brought out my inner-kid. "Geeze, why didn't they have these when I was a kid?" My wife rolled her eyes but smiled. The season was fun, and all was well.

My favorite store in the mall was a big chain bookstore. I always found something cool on the 50% discount rack. Sheila was by my side and we were chatting as we walked, listening to Christmas music.

We turned a corner and I stopped dead in my tracks. My knees started to buckle, and the room spun for a second. I held her shoulder to steady myself and turned away.

Puzzled she asked, "What's wrong with you?"

Without a word I turned around and headed for the door.

Concerned I might be ill, Sheila caught up with me. "Terry, what the hell? Are you sick?"

A wave of nausea washed over me. I leaned against the wall and asked her, "Please, just give me a moment." When I caught my breath I asked her, "Holy shit did you see that? I can't believe it! It was just suddenly in my face! I'm so sorry that I startled you."

"Okay, oh my God you're sweating! Who was in your face? What happened?" She was puzzled and genuinely concerned.

"There's a hardcover book in there. It's on a table at the end cap. Go look at it. You'll see. Just go look at it. I'll hang right here and wait for you," I said. I was certain she'd come back and agree that the images were frightening.

Back in the bookstore she found what had scared me so badly. The face of an alien on the cover of a book. It was identical to the drawings I made back in 1977 and 1979. It was same pointed chin the shape of the head. It had just a slit for a mouth and no discernable ears. It was the same! That meant someone else knew!

She felt unsettled by the image too. But she was far less panicked. She understood. Sheila had comforted me when those images haunted my dreams.

Always supportive, she offered, "Do you want a coffee?"

"Yes, but only if you're buying," I said, admitting I had literally spent my last dollar.

We sat down and talked about an event that happened ten years prior. This was a topic we very rarely discussed. But now it was on the table for discussion. I hoped the discussion would be brief. No matter how much discomfort it caused us, discussing it was the right thing to do. We would talk briefly about the happenings in 1977 and how it had changed both of us. Then we could close the book and go on with our lives.

Just four months earlier we were in the same mall when I passed a widow display being set up. It was a clothing store for women. There were four mannequins and they were all unclothed from the waist up and made of molded plastic. They scared the hell out of me for some reason. I felt panic overtake me. I told my wife about the anxiety and asked if we could please leave. She was annoyed, and we cut that shopping trip short. We didn't discuss it at the time.

It's not like being scared by someone in hiding who jumps out and yells, "Boo!" Sure, you're startled. Your heart races for a minute and everyone has a good laugh at your expense.

This is a totally different experience. There was no incident to startle me. No one yelled boo. This was a process outside of my control. It was a physiological reaction to a visual stimulus. The mannequin heads and the book cover triggered something that startled me to the point of panic. I calmed down and my heart stopped racing, but I was left with an overwhelming sense of dread.

The panic is hard to describe if you've never experienced it. It's a feeling that something awful is about to happen. I'd compare it to sitting in a stalled car on the railroad tracks while a speeding freight train rounds the bend. That level of anxiety usually took a day or two to completely abate.

I sipped my coffee and calmed myself. Again, I was compelled to say, "Sorry."

"It's okay, but Terry, this is just like the mannequin heads that freaked you out a few weeks back. It's just not healthy. You're a grown man with a family and a career. It doesn't happen very often, but you have meltdowns in the mall!" she said. She held my hand and we were both quiet for a moment. I'm certain we both had the same thought, 1977.

Once more I felt the need to justify my actions. "We just turned a corner and bam! It was right in my face; it was the abruptness of seeing the image that startled me so badly," I said. I apologized again for scaring her.

She understood. Sadly, I bet many marriages don't survive such events. I was so fortunate to have married someone so understanding.

In all our years of marriage, we'd never discussed my experiences as a child. But she knew the story. Family secrets are hard kept. She knew I saw a UFO when I was a child back in 1963. My sister had told her the whole story including the fallout in the form of nightmares. It turned out to be helpful in the long run.

She offered a suggestion, "See our doctor; we have terrific health insurance. Get a referral to a counselor and talk to someone. Maybe you can come to terms with this and put your nightmares to bed." We both laughed at her inadvertent pun. I had to admit, it sounded like a good idea when she said it.

For the most part, my life wasn't disrupted by my past encounters. There was sometimes an inexplicable drop of blood on my pillowcase. A single nightmare a year if that. There was the occasional meltdown in a shopping mall when a mannequin head or a book cover triggered a panic attack. There was also an inexplicable discomfort when in the presence of Asian women, particularly elderly Asian women.

I told her I'd consider the counseling idea. But, soon I began to see it as an overreaction. I wanted to minimize the incident. I really didn't have spare time to devote to doctor appointments.

I followed up on the idea for her peace of mind, for the sake of family harmony. There was no way I could speak to our family doctor. Especially if I were to be totally candid. I doubted I could do it. Instead, I simply asked for a referral and booked an appointment to see a therapist. My insurance company would pay for ten visits. Surely more than enough. I went through the list of approved therapists covered by my health plan and chose the one nearest my office. Her name was Elizabeth something, she was four blocks from my downtown office.

A week later I made my way to her office. I had just a three-minute wait before she called my name. Her office was typical. I noted her credentials as a master's degree in clinical social work MSW from Pennsylvania State. We exchanged the routine introductory politeness. Her name was Elizabeth, but she preferred to be called "Beth."

Before we could begin, she required that I take a battery of tests. I took an MMPI or Minnesota Multiphasic Personality Inventory and another test I was unfamiliar with. I saw it as a waste of an entire session.

I guess the tests were important. It made sense to rule out an underlying psychosis or mental illness. If you're suffering from a mental illness can you see it when you look at your reflection in the mirror? Or is it only apparent to those around you? How do you know?

At our next session she walked me through my test results. She described them as significant in a couple ways. I had elevated levels of anxiety and paranoia. Not to the point of psychosis, but more than average. That was welcome news.

"Terry, people who have lived through a traumatic event have similar symptoms and similar test scores. Your test scores were consistent with men and women suffering from post traumatic stress disorder commonly referred to as PTSD."

"Yes, I've heard of PTSD."

"Terry, I'd like to know about your military service. Were you in combat?"

"Fortunately, I never left the States," I replied.

"Terry, you've experienced a trauma in your life. We don't have to discuss the details if you don't want to. But can you tell me what happened to you?"

"Beth, I ..." I hesitated.

A long pause filled the room. It made me uncomfortable. Maybe that was her intent. Then I told her about the two flying saucers I saw as a child. But 1977 event was strictly out of bounds. No way in hell would we discuss that event!

"Beth, I had two very strange UFOs sightings in my early childhood. Everything else in my life is fine."

"Yes, go on," she said. I felt pressured to continue.

"I have frightening thoughts … intrusive thoughts. I also have horrible nightmares—just one or two a year now. And sometimes I'll see something that triggers a panic episode. That's the reason I'm here. The panic attacks are uncontrollable and just hell to experience."

"Yes, they are hell. That's very typical of PTSD. How do you tell the difference between an intrusive thought and a flashback?" Beth asked.

"A flashback is usually triggered by something that brings back a flood of unwelcome images like the face on the jacket cover of a book. The intrusive thoughts don't usually have a "trigger" or the same intense imagery. They seem to suddenly cross my mind and it's difficult to shut them off. I know I'm recalling events from the past, but the anxiety is almost as bad as when it happened."

"Could you tell me what happened during your last panic episode? Can we start there?" she asked hoping to move forward.

I told her about the meltdown I had in the bookstore and the mannequin heads.

Beth said, "I can understand how uncomfortable that must have been."

"Okay …" was all I had to offer. I sincerely doubted she understood my discomfort.

She said, "I believe your panic attacks are genuine and can make it hard to function at times. You saw or experienced something so horrible that it left a scar on your psyche. I think we can work together. I can teach you some simple techniques to better cope with this problem. You can learn to live with this."

I asked, "Beth you tell me you ruled out a mental illness and personality disorders. I am sane at least as far as the legal definition of the term is concerned, is that true?"

"Yes, Terry that's accurate in my opinion."

"But I am likely suffering from PTSD as an after effect of some occurrence. Am I right so far?"

"Yes, that's correct too," she said. I heard the acoustics in the room change. Her voice was now louder.

I abruptly felt annoyed with Beth. There was just something about the woman's tone of voice that irritated me. I couldn't identify exactly what quality in her voice I found irksome, but she was hard to listen too. The office seemed smaller than I remembered during my first visit too. It was just a place I'd rather not be.

"Can you tell me about the incident that brought you here today? I believe you told me there was an incident while in the mall? Tell me about that experience. Did that experience tip the scale for you? Is that what brought you here?" Beth asked.

I believe she could sense my growing anxiety.

"It was my wife's idea to speak with someone," I said. Then I opened-up and explained the two incidents in the mall. I gave her all the details this time. How I felt panicked at the sight of the face on the book cover and the mannequins. I was also candid with her about the conversation my wife and I had after the last event.

"I can see a similarity in those two images. Terry, do you see anything in common between what hurt so badly in your past and the things that scared you in the mall? Do they have something in common?" Beth asked.

I felt my anxiety growing. "The commonality between the two is obvious! Aside from that? Well I saw a UFO when I was eight and another when I was eleven. I also had an experience back in 1977 when I was in the Air Force," I said before realizing it!

Oops! I had resolved not to talk about the 1977 incident! We wouldn't go there, not at all damn it. But it was done and there's no way to take back what I said.

"Okay Terry, then how do those incidents from your past relate to what's going on today?"

I said, "Beth, I saw those flying saucers not just once but a couple times."

"That's what scared you so badly?" she asked. I'm sure she was confused with my abrupt change of topic onto flying saucers and away from 1977.

"No!" I raised my voice slightly. I began to feel angry for no reason. Beth was momentarily taken aback. I was shaking now and sweating. I didn't know how to answer her question. This began to feel amazingly familiar. It was like I was reliving my experience with our family doctor back in 1963. The doctor I labeled "asshole." The same guy who told me, "Nothing in the sky can hurt you." Maybe I saw her like the doctor who violated my trust?

Beth continued to probe, "Then what was it Terry? What scared you? Something scared you and it's connected to your UFO sightings."

I had no answer. We were both quiet for a minute or two, each waiting for the other to speak.

Seizing the initiative, Beth asked, "What do you see when you have flashbacks? Do the flashbacks take you back to the incident? What do you remember?"

"No Beth, I don't remember much of anything." Truthfully, I didn't remember much! But her question triggered anxiety. Not panic, but anxiety. I didn't know it at the time, but I'd been programmed to forget and to not discuss or explore the events from 1977.

"I'm sorry Beth. I didn't mean to raise my voice earlier." I said apologetically.

Mentally, I felt guilty and ashamed for some inexplicable reason. I felt like I had just revealed a clandestine family secret. I felt ill and waves of nausea turned over in my stomach. I was trembling. I wondered if she could sense how badly I felt at that moment.

She said, "Terry it's okay. You're obviously hurting. Would you like to learn some techniques to help you deal with this anxiety? I can teach you."

I was quick to reply, "Look Beth, you're very kind and I appreciate your patience. I don't think I can remember and I'm not sure I want to remember. Can we quit for today?" I stood.

"Of course!" she said. "I'll see you next Wednesday then?" She smiled and held out her right hand.

I didn't want her to feel my hand was shaking and my palm was sweaty. What followed was an awkward exchange back and forth. Eventually we managed to make contact for a brief handshake. I couldn't look her in the eye.

"Yes, thank you Beth," and I left her office. I think we both knew I wasn't coming back. I raced to my car and felt very good. As I climbed into my car I said under my breath, "That was a very close call."

But in retrospect, a close call from what? Why did I feel like I had just dodged a bullet? Why did I need to run away? I also felt guilt for no reason. It was a short drive home. I had to tell Sheila something. I decided to be upbeat.

"My tests showed no evidence of severe mental illness. It was all very positive!" I said convincingly.

"Well that's good news! I'm glad you went for a second session. So, tell me all about it."

"The therapist taught me some techniques to manage my anxiety. I'm satisfied. I think we're done!" I said. I lied. I lied to my closest friend and confidant. I knew the importance of truth.

She was skeptical, but we dropped the subject. The next day I called and cancelled my appointment with Beth's receptionist. I thought, that's the end of that.

A week later Beth called me at my office, "Terry, I've cancelled your appointment. I appreciate the courtesy of your call."

"You're welcome Beth. No-shows are a problem in my practice too."

"Terry, I think therapy would be of help to you. It's okay if you don't wish to see me again really. That's your choice."

"Thank you, Beth."

"The reason for my call is to see if you'd be interested in speaking to a colleague of mine?"

I asked her, "What can he do for me that you can't?"

Beth explained, "He's a clinical psychologist. He won't charge you for his time until your insurance kicks in and I believe he's on your list of authorized providers. Would you be interested in speaking with him? I think he could help you. He works with clients who've experienced similar types of things. His name is Dr. Paul Miller. I'll leave you his number."

"Sure, go ahead Beth, I have a pen."

I jotted it down on my calendar and said, "Thank you Beth."

"Terry, if I have your permission I'll give Dr. Miller the bare bones of your encounter and share your test results. That might save some time. Dr. Miller admits openly that he had an experience of his own. He works with many clients who've seen UFOs and had similar experiences," she said. I knew her intent was to be helpful.

"No Beth, thank you. I'll just call him myself, I said."

The next morning, I was on the phone with someone. I don't remember the call. It was something routine. I caught myself staring at this doctor's phone number on the margin of my calendar.

In the middle of the phone call, with my fountain pen I began to change the first digit from a "5" to an "S." It wasn't a conscious thought, it was just doodling. It was my usual habit to doodle on my calendar and drive my poor secretary crazy when she needed it.

While we continued with our conversation I moved to the second digit. The numeral "1" in the Michigan 517 area code. Without much thought I placed a line across the top and a "1" became the letter "T." I finished my call and hung up to stare out of the window. My mind was a blank slate. It was snowing heavily, and I watched the big flakes pile up.

Pen still in hand, I drew a curved line to close the numeral "7" turning it into the letter "O." Moving on it was a more difficult matter, but I changed the "4" into a lower case "P." With my fountain pen, I then obliterated the remaining seven digits under a layer of deep blue ink. What was left was now four letters. I had spelled "STOP."

I stared at it for a moment and laughed. For some reason it cracked me up. I turned the page in my calendar prematurely, to begin a new day.

My Last Ride

We lived in the suburbs, but if you traveled thirty minutes or so there were some beautiful country back roads with great scenery. The colors were spectacular, especially in autumn. September and October have always been my favorite month.

My love of motorbikes goes back to my teenage years. Especially back in the days when I was young and immortal. Now that I'm a little older and wiser I know the risks outweigh the pleasure. As we age I think it's normal to occasionally think about our own mortality. I don't know what awaits us after death but I'm in no hurry to find out. A comedian said, "All men must die. I was just hoping for an exception." There are no exceptions.

I am a creature of habit. My weekly routine in September and October was to rise around 7:30 AM on Sunday mornings. Weather permitting; I'd quietly dress in my motorcycle gear and leather jacket. Roll my bike down the driveway into the street before starting the engine. I didn't want to wake the family by revving the engine. Then I would ride for the pleasure of it. I'd take a two or three-hour motorcycle trip while my wife and kids slept-in.

It was time for myself. I cruised the back roads and enjoyed the exhilaration of the speed and the wind. It was fun. I might think about work at the office or I might think of nothing at all. Some days, like that day, I just enjoyed the experience.

I timed my rides to get me back home no later than 11:00 AM. That gave me time to make pancakes for Sunday breakfast. I'd wait until I was out of the subdivision to decide which route suited my taste for the day's ride.

There were three routes in my playbook. They all took me through areas with minimal traffic and beautiful fall scenery. Unless I was stuck at a railroad crossing waiting for 100 boxcar-loads of coal to pass I was home by 10:30 to 11:00 at the latest. I am known for being punctual.

This fall day I took a two-lane blacktop road that wound through mostly cornfields and wooded areas. I just rode and enjoyed my morning.

Some guys hunt and some guys fish. I road my motorcycles. Everyone who works hard deserves a pastime. It was cheaper than golf.

Daydreaming and cruising along, I suddenly found myself on a gravel road! I stopped immediately. I took off my helmet and looked around hunting for landmarks to get my bearings. I was about a mile off blacktop. I'd traveled this route a dozen times or more. This time, for whatever reason, I had unintentionally turned off the blacktop about a mile back and was on gravel! That was a big deal.

It's dangerous to ride on gravel. Plus, I treated my motorcycle like some guys treat their Corvette. I washed and waxed it regularly and I never took my bike on gravel roads.

It was also bad for my motorcycle. I wouldn't risk a paint chip from the rocks! A blemished paintjob from a pebble would be a disaster.

But here I was, on a dusty, gravel farm road that went nowhere. I chided myself for not paying better attention. I couldn't even recall what kept my mind so preoccupied.

I turned the bike around and headed the short mile back to asphalt. I picked up where I had left off and finished my motorcycle ride. I rolled up my driveway and headed inside to start breakfast. Instead of my usual greeting, I was met by a tearful wife.

"Where the hell have you been? I've been worried sick! I called the police and asked if they had responded to any accidents. I was just about to get in the car and hunt for you! I was afraid you ran off the road somewhere and might be hurt! Where did you go?" she asked, tears rolling down her cheeks.

"The usual," I said defensively! "What's wrong with you?"

"It's 12:30! That's what's wrong with me! Where have you been for two hours?"

It was unbelievable! I was as clueless as she was. I was sometimes the absent-minded professor type misplacing my car keys or my wallet. That was nothing new.

I hadn't stopped that day, not even for gas. There were no coal trains crossing my path that day. The only exception to my normal ride was the one-mile wrong turn down some farm road and the few minutes it took to get back onto blacktop. That couldn't account for more than ten minutes.

The clock on the wall, the sun in the sky, and the lack of cartoons blaring on the TV all confirmed that I was two hours late! I went out and looked my bike over. It was dustier than usual. That was expected from the short trip on gravel. Glancing at my wrist, my timepiece clearly read 12:50. I should have arrived home between 10:30 and 11:00 AM. I was shocked!

The odometer was no help. I didn't keep track of the miles since it was a familiar route. I never checked the time because the ride was my watch. To check my wristwatch would have involved taking one hand off the handlebars and hunting for a watch under leather gloves and a long leather sleeve.

All I could do was apologize profusely. Pancakes were off the menu today. My wife's initial fear for my safety now turned into justified anger. I was baffled too. I had no defense or explanation.

I reviewed the course of the ride in my head. I kept coming back to the only variable. A short diversion down that gravel farm road. There was no reason why I shouldn't have arrived back home at 10:30 AM!

Now was not the time to approach my wife. We were both emotional. This would take some time for things to calm down.

Later that afternoon we sat and talked. I'd sell my bike before I'd allow it to cause trouble in my marriage.

She accepted my apology. I also told her I'd put the bike up for sale. It was time.

Before we had finished, she said she'd had an odd experience herself on the night before. She said she'd save that for later, but in the meanwhile she had an idea she was eager to discuss.

"Could you have had an experience like Betty and Barney Hill," she asked?

A few years earlier she had read an account of a New Hampshire couple in a reputable news magazine. After our experiences from 1977, nothing seemed too far-fetched as to be outside the realm of possibility. I was surprised she even thought about it. We simply didn't discuss the topic and here she was asking me to pursue it?

Grasping for anything to help me make sense of what happened, I agreed, "Sure, I can't rule that out." But secretly, I thought to myself there's a reasonable explanation for this mess. I just had to review my ride step-by-step and an explanation would surface. One never did.

I wanted to make peace with my wife. The Hill's had a very similar experience, so I could examine their plight as a remote possibility.

I asked her, "By any chance did you happen to save that magazine?"

She did! Of course, she did. I was skeptical about the article at first but after the first couple pages, I was hooked. I eagerly read every word. It is an incredible story.

Betty and Barney Hill were the couple whose case coined the phrase, "missing time" as used in UFO terminology. The Hills were also the first couple to go public with their story of an alien spacecraft and an abduction experience. Their story made worldwide press. In case you're not familiar, here's a brief synopsis of their story.

In September 1961, the Hills lost three hours of time on a road trip by car. Their usual seven-hour drive through a forested area of New Hampshire took ten hours! They were traveling at night on a route they'd traveled many times before. They were never lost; they never made a wrong turn or broke down with car trouble.

Neither of them had an explanation. Both were sick for a few days when they got home. Their mechanical watches had stopped working and there was a strange powder-like stain on Betty's dress. Barney noticed the tops of his shoes were scuffed. The strap on his binoculars had broken, and there was damage to the trunk of their car. Damage that wasn't there when Barney loaded their suitcases hours earlier.

They were both sick when they arrived home. They sought medical help weeks later, when Betty's nightmares became unbearable. Eventually, they were referred to a psychiatrist named Dr. Stephens. Stephens was a medical doctor and a practicing psychiatrist who sometimes used hypnosis in treating patients.

Dr. Stephens suggested a hypnosis session. He thought it might help the Hill's to recall details about what happened that evening, and account for the missing time. When they were referred to Dr. Stephens, neither one had a recollection of what had happened during the three hours that were just gone. Betty recalled seeing a strange star in the sky but that was all.

The Hills agreed to hypnosis, and what was revealed was incredible. I encourage you to read the transcripts. Their hypnosis sessions were all recorded, and a copy of the transcript is easily found online.

If you're the least bit interested, I encourage you to read them. The transcripts describe a horrific experience at the hand of alien beings. They were abducted and taken aboard a spacecraft against their will. These were all memories of real events that had somehow been suppressed from their consciousness.

It was hard to believe these two very credible people would corroborate to pull-off such an outrageous hoax. They appeared to have lost much more than they gained from the experience.

They said when they were aboard the spacecraft, they were examined and suffered painful medical procedures performed by non-human entities. Betty recalled that one of the beings held an instrument she described as resembling a knitting needle. He wanted to stick it into Betty's navel. She cried and begged him not to do it. The fear in her voice is palpable. It must be heard to grasp the terror she experienced.

Betty could recall one of the entities showing her a star chart and explaining it's where they came from. With pen and paper, she drew it from memory when she got home but didn't recognize its significance. She put it aside.

Years later, a respected astronomer would match Betty's star map to the known universe and against the odds, he found a perfect match!

Sure, someone could argue with the number of stars in the sky if you look hard enough you should be able to match any configuration. What amazes me is that she was able to recall the image at all!

Whenever Sheila and I discussed my 1977 encounter, the nightmares would return without fail. My poor wife was exhausted from years of being rudely awakened by her husband's screams at 3:00 AM. Sheets soaked in sweat and a pillowcase with a drop of blood now and then. She was tired of it. So instead, I turned my attention to the Hill's encounter, objectively. I wouldn't seek parallels to what bits I could remember from my own experience. Instead, I read it for amusement and didn't dwell on it.

After ruling out a stroke, epilepsy, and all the other possibilities we could think of short of temporary madness, an alien abduction seemed like a viable explanation.

Despite the focus of this book and my past experiences, I'm not someone who jumps to a paranormal explanation for every inexplicable event. I try to approach problems the way I practice law: slowly and systematically and examining all possibilities before reaching a conclusion.

Occam's razor is a 14th century approach to problem solving. The phrase was coined by a gentleman named William of Ockham in the 14th century. In Latin it's "lex parsimoniae" or the law of parsimony. I know. Too much information.

In plain English, it's a problem-solving principle that works like this. First identify every possible explanation and investigate each one carefully and thoroughly. Usually the simplest explanation will answer the question.

Once you've ruled out the impossible, and you're left with just one explanation, that's your answer. No matter how extraordinary it might sound, that is your answer.

I hated to face it, but it made sense. If any of this stuff makes sense. It could account for the two hours that are missing from my trip.

I admitted alien abduction was a possibility I couldn't dismiss out of hand. But I wasn't willing to give it the analysis it deserved. I didn't want to suffer the repercussions that accompanied dwelling on the past.

"Thank you, Sheila. That's fascinating," I said. I handed her magazine back.

We wordlessly agreed whatever the reason for the two-hour gap we'd drop it there.

Then I remembered. "Sheila, you said you had an odd experience of your own to tell me about."

She began with "Now, I know this is hard to believe ..."

I was shaking my head "No." We live in a world full of oddities. She didn't need to preface her story or qualify her observations.

In a calm and almost matter of fact tone of voice she said, "Terry, Saturday night, I woke up to see a three-foot tall woman standing at the end of the bed. I remember reaching for you and you were gone. It was the middle of the night and I have no idea what time it was."

"What did she look like? Can you draw her?" I asked.

"I'll try, but first just let me finish. This woman wore a dark hooded robe of some kind tied at the waist with a cord. The hood covered most of her head. Her eyes were big. Terry, they were almost as big as that picture on the book cover. I mean the one that scared you at the mall. She was between the foot of our bed and the window, so it was hard to see her clearly in silhouette. But I saw her clear enough!"

I said, "Go on. What else can you remember?"

"I wasn't scared! I wasn't anything! She just looked at me and I heard her voice inside my head. Her lips never moved. She told me, 'Everything is okay go back to sleep.' Just those seven words. I should have screamed. She told me, 'Everything is okay go back to sleep.' That's what I did. The next morning, I woke up and wondered if maybe it had been a dream. But it was so real." We were both lost in thought for a moment. She looked to me for validation, "Terry, I believe this really happened." As an afterthought she added, "Oh, and one more thing to add. When I got the laundry together there was a drop of blood on your pillowcase again this morning."

I didn't know it at the time, but I'd been programmed. We'd been programmed. So be it. Deep down I knew that I wasn't supposed to talk about them. I knew these things have rules. I either followed the rules or risked being punished.

They are not benevolent space-brothers. They have an agenda alright, but it's not a cure for cancer or to give us a new source of energy to replace petroleum. Their agenda is purely pragmatic. They are 100% goal driven.

I always wondered: if they share their technology with us, what do we give in return? What's the quid pro quo?

I decided to put my bike up for sale the following week. I'd miss riding but that fear of being in open spaces had returned. At least I was spared weeks of horrific nightmares this time.

What happened to me during those lost hours? It would be years before I found out.

Sheryl

A significant event occurred in 1977 when I was a young NCO in the United States Air Force. It's a complex story and before I revisit it I'd like to share with you someone else's story that is directly related to mine. Her story bolsters mine. It is true, and I think you'll find it fascinating.

It belonged to a client from my legal practice. I'll protect her privacy by calling her Sheryl, and I'll alter the location a bit. But otherwise, this is the truthful telling of Sheryl's bizarre tale and my involvement.

I was in the office on a Friday morning and I took an early telephone call. It was just 7:30 AM. I was in the office early to prepare for a 9:00 AM hearing. Always eager for new business, I answered the phone on the first ring.

It was from a newly retired General Motors factory worker named Sheryl. She said an old friend of hers from the car plant had referred me. She said I was recommended because I was an "an honest lawyer." That made my day.

I understood the importance of referrals. I wanted my name to pop up when a client, or a client's friend or relative, found themselves in trouble. It seemed that an awful lot of people had problems of one kind or another. But for me, it's what I referred to as a "happy problem." My success was the product of other's misfortune. Much like driving an ambulance.

Sheryl had plenty to say. I broke into her rant to say, "Whoa, whoa, slower please I'm having trouble following you." I was scribbling notes onto a legal pad and trying to find out the nature of her problem. I told her, "Please Madam, save the details for a face-to-face meeting. For now, just tell me. What is your problem?"

Slowing her speech, she complained about neighbors trespassing on her property at night. She claimed that they shined bright lights into her bedroom window. Waking her up at night and scaring her. That was all.

A simple trespass onto her property was a legitimate legal issue. I bet there's a whole lot more to this story. There always is. I reject cases if there are no legal issues, as any ethical lawyer should. Lots of people seek legal help for family problems, troublesome neighbors and hurt feelings. There are TV judges and psychologist to address those issues.

We discussed my fee structure. She asked to schedule an appointment, preferably in the afternoon, but soon. Fortunately, I had a slot open the following Monday. I was free for the entire day after 3:00 in the afternoon.

She agreed to be at my office at 3:00 Monday afternoon. I asked her to write out a brief narrative of the events including a list of the names and addresses of everyone involved.

I was intrigued by the urgency in her voice. Neighbor to neighbor feuds can sometimes end with people being hurt or worse. It's the reason so many police officers are wounded or killed when responding to domestic disturbance calls.

Before hanging up, I felt it wise to offer some advice. I said, "Sheryl, I don't know what may have happened to make this matter urgent today. But remember, you can always call 911 if you feel threatened and the police will respond."

She said simply, "Okay" and I ended the call.

Sheryl arrived 15 minutes early and sat in the waiting room. She looked things over and flipped through a movie magazine, all the while careful not to loosen the grip she held on her purse. It was on her lap and held firmly in place with one hand juggling the magazine with the other. She was very disappointed to learn we were a nonsmoking building.

Having studied psychology, I was keen on watching people for nonverbal cues. I studied her posture and appearance. Body language speaks volumes, as does choice of attire. I sized up Sheryl as eccentric. Her eccentricity would prove to be off the chart.

She was well groomed but wore a hand knitted sweater that was outdated and too small for her large frame. She wore a garish blouse with a checkered pattern of alternating browns and orange. The pattern on her pantsuit was brown and tan, with horizontal stripes. She completed the outfit with a sturdy pair of white nursing style shoes. Her hair had been curled into a style reminiscent of what my sisters wore in the late 60s.

This should be interesting, I thought to myself. That would turn out to be an understatement. Just not in a way I could have ever guessed.

Thank God it was a slow day. With luck, I could be out of the office by 4:00 and free to enjoy an abbreviated Monday. There would be plenty of long days to balance the scale.

I went down the short stairwell and introduced myself. She shook my hand in a masculine manner with eye contact but no smile. She followed as we headed to my office. I asked, "Can I get you a cup of coffee?"

"No thank you, it's too late in the day," she said.

I was grateful. She did not look like someone who needed caffeine.

Once inside my office I shut the office door as always. I noticed her eyes darting as she looked over the office. Before being seated she put on a pair of drugstore glasses and inspected my law degree and license to practice.

I did my best to engage her in small talk without much success.

I noticed she kept a death-grip on that purse. It was planted square on her lap and not once did she set it on the floor. I took that to mean she's cautious.

With the small talk going nowhere I decided to get down to business. I asked, "Okay Sheryl, did you bring a brief narrative with names and addresses of your problem neighbors?"

"No, I can tell you everything you need to know," Sheryl said.

I was annoyed. I asked her to please tell me the neighbor's name, so I could be certain there was no conflict of interest. There wasn't.

Probing, I asked her to tell me all about her neighbors, the trespass and lights shined in her window. "Can you tell me about that I asked?"

Ignoring my question, she made eye contact and in a serious tone and asked, "Can I trust you Mr. Lovelace? I need someone to talk to. I need someone who won't think I'm crazy and listen to me?"

Her question struck me as somewhat odd. I tried to size up her mental status. She seemed fully functional but impaired in some way. I'm not a psychologist. It didn't take a psychologist to tell that she had problems.

Alarm bells rang in my head. I was cautious about dealing with the mentally ill. I preferred to represent them through a guardian if one had been appointed by the court. I also glanced at my watch. I couldn't listen to a half-hour of nonsense. But I pressed on.

"Yes, you can trust me. Everything you tell me is held in strict confidence," I said. I assured her that I would not lie to her. I promised to keep her informed of everything happening with her case. There would be no surprises. I would take no action in her case without her prior approval.

She nodded and said she understood. She was a bit more relaxed. I gave her a written fee agreement to read. She went through it line by line making certain she understood. She would need to pay some money up front if she decided I could help her with whatever was going on with the neighbors.

In a casual voice I asked her, "Sheryl, do you handle all your own financial affairs?"

Offended by my question she spat back, "I handle all of my own money if that's what you mean!"

I ignored it and continued.

With the formalities finished I asked her again, "Now Sheryl, please tell me about your problem and I'll see what I can do to help?"

She said, "Okay but you're not going to charge me a lot of money, are you?"

I said "Sheryl, if after we talk today I don't think you have a legal matter that I can help you with or if you can't afford the fee there will be no charge for today's visit. If your neighbors are causing you a problem sometimes a stern letter from a lawyer can end the matter. That would be a very affordable option."

That seemed to satisfy her. She began sheepishly. She said, "Well I haven't been exactly honest with you, it's not my neighbors Mr. Lovelace. I believe it is aliens. I'm being visited by them. Do you believe in aliens?"

I nearly choked on my bottled water. Surely, I misunderstood. Did that come out of her mouth? I was rattled by her question. It took me a moment to regain my composure.

"I'm sorry, I want to be clear. Sheryl you're talking about an immigration issue here? Are these people that trespass and shine lights through your window at night, are they from another country and here to work in the United States illegally?"

She looked confused for a moment and said firmly, "No! I am talking about men who come here from outer space in a flying saucer. Sometimes in a great big ball looking thing too. They shine white orange and green lights in my bedroom window. Sometimes red lights too. Do you believe in visitors from outer space?"

My thoughts flashed back to a winter morning at about 3:00 AM in 1966. I shook off the memory and continued. I tried very hard to not appear ruffled by her statements.

Calmly I said, "Sheryl, my beliefs aren't relevant, but yes I believe there's life in this great big universe. Now go on please. I'm listening to you. I'm not judging you in any way. Tell me the truth and I'll see if I can help you."

She dropped her voice to just above a whisper, "They come in a flying saucer with lights and they come onto my property. They shine bright lights in my bedroom window at night and they scare me. Now I believe they've been inside my house!" She looked very frightened.

"What makes you think that they've been in your home?" I asked. She was visibly trembling. It was apparent that something had scared this woman out of her wits.

"Well what scared me the most was the little person! I saw it just out of the corner of my eye. I saw it dart past my bedroom door and it scared me. Oh, they make my skin crawl!"

I said, "I understand. Please go on." I knew this wasn't a legal problem. Still I really wanted to do something to help this woman if possible. Because I know what it's like to see something, to be very afraid and have no one believe you. But I'm not a mental health professional. This was dangerous territory.

"They scare me. The police won't come anymore, and they think I'm crazy," she said. I think she was a little embarrassed. She searched my face for any sign of empathy or understanding.

"Sheryl, I don't think you have a legitimate legal issue here. I don't know what I can do to help you if the problem doesn't originate with your next-door neighbors?"

"So, you can't help me either?" she said. She was crestfallen.

I said, "I'm so sorry." It was the best I could offer her.

She pulled her chair back to leave.

I remained seated. "Sheryl there's no charge for our visit today. But I do have an idea. Just sit down and listen for a moment. Do you have a nice camera?"

She sat back down and looked puzzled but eager to hear what I had to say. She shook her head. She asked, "No, why do you ask?"

I explained, "Then go to a pawn shop or somewhere and buy yourself a decent 35mm camera, one with a telephoto lens if possible, and a tripod. You don't need to spend a lot of money. Do you have a friend or a relative that knows about cameras?"

She thought for a minute and said, "Yes, I have a niece who'd help me I bet. She loves her Aunt Sheryl. She knows all about photography." She was smiling now for the first time. I could see she had wheels turning.

"Set your camera on the tripod aim it out the window that faces the spot where the spaceship usually lands. Make sure you have it focused on the area where the flying saucer lands. The next time the aliens come back you get as many pictures of them as you can. Be sure and buy film made to work in poorly lighted conditions. Ask the store clerk for help choosing film. Usually someone can give you advice. Maybe your niece will help you. Come back and see me when you get them on film. Bring me the pictures and we can consider our next step. Does that sound fair?"

"Oh yes, thank you. What's our next step then?" she asked.

I didn't answer her because I didn't have the slightest idea what the next step might be. But it was all I could think of. It's questionable ethics maybe. But I thought maybe this will put the issue to bed for her. I at least offered her an active plan to battle her problem. It couldn't hurt.

"Oh, what a marvelous idea!" Sheryl said. She was beaming. She was thrilled with the idea. I also think she was just happy that someone listened to her and offered a solution of sorts. She thanked me repeatedly and I escorted her to the front door.

Before she could drive away I asked her, "Sheryl you should talk to your doctor too. Will you do that for me please?"

She didn't reply. She hopped into her truck fired up a cigarette and was gone.

I thought, "That's the last I'll ever see of Sheryl." I felt like I did the right thing. I certainly did her no harm. I went back to work now half-an hour behind.

I scolded myself for playing therapist instead of practicing law.

A month later my secretary buzzed me. "There's a Sheryl on line one. She said she talked to you a couple weeks ago and she has some big news."

Rolling my eyes, I said aloud, "Oh my God here we go!" I picked up the phone, "This is Mr. Lovelace."

A very agitated Sheryl was on the line. Just like last time she spoke so fast I couldn't make out what she was saying. I asked her to please, slow down.

As usual she began in a rant, "This is Sheryl Foster from Benton. I did it Mr. Lovelace! I finally got some real pictures of the aliens. Oh, I'm so excited! I got a picture of their spaceship. I even got pictures of them in my backyard, walking down the train tracks behind the house, and …. Oh, I want to nail these little bastards!"

I started to say something, but she cut me off in mid-sentence. At least she dialed-down her speed so I could understand her.

"I took your advice Mr. Lovelace. My niece liked the idea too! She helped me set it all up. Then I waited. I'll be damned, two nights ago they came back! I got pictures of the little sons-of-bitches and their spaceship too. Do you want to see the pictures?"

I was unsure what to do. I was curious as hell. What the hell did she see? And I wanted to see what this woman photographed. Her timing was terrible. I had an hour and thirty minutes of time devoted to writing a brief. I could slide her into that slot and finish my brief after dinner.

I told her, "Yes bring the pictures! Come right on over."

She exclaimed, "Oh, wonderful, I'm on my way!"

Before she could hang up I told her, "Bring in the photographs and the negatives together. Keep them in the drugstore package along with your receipt if possible. Did your camera print the date on the back of each picture?"

"Oh yes they show the time too. You'll see! My niece set up my camera to do all that. I'm on my way now."

I told her goodbye and hung up. I asked my law clerk to stick around for just a bit. While waiting I wondered. What the hell did this woman photograph? Maybe we could sell them to a tabloid paper? Can I even do that ethically?

If she would agree to it there'd be no harm. I would insist that her niece be a party to the whole affair. I didn't want to be accused of taking advantage of this fragile and vulnerable woman. What would my colleagues think? Could I be exploiting her? I was getting way ahead of myself.

This was time I could use productively. But I also thought, who knows, this could be profitable and helpful for both of us.

Sheryl must have made the drive doing 90 mph. Fifteen minutes later she arrived. I was downstairs waiting for her. She snuffed out her cigarette on my wooden front porch and came inside heading straight for the stairs. I followed behind her.

I'd given this some forethought. When we reached the second-floor landing I said, "Let's go into my conference room with the large table instead of the smaller desk top in my office. The table is much bigger, and we can lay everything out in front of us!"

She hesitated, "Is it safe?" Her comment would only make sense if spoken by one abductee to another. To put her at ease I said, "Give me just a minute to shut the drapes and look things over. Just to be sure. Please wait right here for me."

She cautioned, "Make sure you check the closet!"

After a minute or two I came back out. In a serious tone of voice, I assured her, "Everything is secure. Come in and I'll shut the door."

She came in and took a chair but only after she had visually inspected the entire conference room. I sat next to her. Her eyes swept the room for a second time before she felt relaxed enough to speak, "Oh, Mr. Lovelace wait till you see these!"

She released the death grip she had on her white plastic purse clicking open the clasp she carefully removed the drugstore photo-packet. The odor of tobacco smoke rose around us. She handled the package like it was dynamite and handed them to me. All the while she was smiling, but I noticed a tremor in her hands that I didn't see many weeks back.

Taking out the photographs I quickly flipped through all twenty-four color photographs. I methodically laid them on the table in the order of the negatives. I numbered each one with pencil on back and kept them in the same order as the negatives. I listed them on my legal pad, plus the date and time. I noticed her photographs were taken over a thirty-hour period. Now, I could study them.

While I was not surprised, I admit I was disappointed. Like a kid getting socks for Christmas disappointment..

Sheryl had managed to photograph her neighbors. They were in a variety of outside activities. She captured them hanging up laundry, gardening and performing an assortment of ordinary outside activities in their own back yards.

There were several shots of high school kids. They were just strolling along the railroad tracks with their backpacks at the far end of her property. A few of the night shots were too blurry to make out much. I saw no one trespass onto her land.

But there was one intriguing photograph that caught my eye. It was the first one she took. I gave it a second careful inspection. It was taken in the dark, but the quality was nearly good. It was an object on the tracks that appeared to be in motion.

I asked, "Did your niece help you find the right kind of film?"

"Oh yes, she's a very sharp girl. She knows all about cameras. She thought it was a good idea to get pictures too."

The shot I found intriguing was focused squarely on the railroad tracks toward the back of her property. It was dark except for a blurred semicircular object. There was a streak of grey light along the side and two smaller green and yellow lights in the center facing the house. It sat squarely on the railroad tracks.

Then I saw one tiny red dot in the pitch-black background. It was high above the image and to the right. It looked out of place. Around the crescent shaped object on the tracks there appeared to be a fog or a mist. It was a solid object in motion, but it was impossible to discern which direction it was traveling.

"Tell me about this one," I asked.

Sheryl said it was the only one she could get of their spacecraft.

I said, "Tell me how it came to your attention."

"It landed on the tracks about 4:30 yesterday morning! Oh, they still scare me so bad! Their lights woke me up again and I followed all the instruction my niece gave me. I took the picture!"

"Why didn't you take more?"

"That was all the pictures. It never crossed my mind. Besides all I wanted to do was go back to sleep. I got the best ones the next day."

Apathy. I completely understood.

I arranged all 24 photographs on the table side by side in sequence. One shot was a photograph of boys walking along the railroad tracks. It was interesting because comparing it to image #1 of the "spaceship," it was the identical location taken in daylight. I compared the two side by side.

I was amazed. I discovered a tiny red dot above the blur of color in the nighttime shot. It matched exactly to the top of a communication tower visible in the distance and just to the right in the daytime photographs. The tower's light was turned off during daylight hours.

Using my desk lamp, I put the two negatives together, one on top of the other and studied them closely. They lined up perfectly. The red dot was smack on top of the tower and gave me a point of reference.

I showed the two photographs to Sheryl and pointed out the communication tower as a point of reference. But she was not overly impressed. She felt the best photograph was the schoolboys walking on the tracks. She insisted, that if you look closely you'd see they were really aliens. I did look closely. Very closely. I didn't see anything that looked like an alien.

I could sense she was becoming frustrated with me. Ethically, I wouldn't lie to her and play along with boys walking on the railroad tracks. But I had learned years earlier not to argue with mental illness.

When I complimented her and praised her for doing such a terrific job her attitude turned on a dime. She was smiling again. Eagerly she said, "So, what's our next move?"

"Yes" I said aloud, "What *is* our next move?"

The room was silent for a long while. I suggested, "Why don't you let me keep copies of about three of your best ones? I'll pay you for the prints and there's no charge for my time today. I'd like to keep the negatives too, just this one strip. You can have them back whenever you like. With your permission I'll show them to some folks who may know what these things are. I promise I'll keep you informed and respect your privacy."

I buzzed my law clerk and asked him run to the drugstore on the corner and make prints of these three pictures from the negative. I handed him a twenty. He glanced at Sheryl and his eyes widened. He knew the matter was emergent. He was off at a trot.

Sheryl and I chatted in my office. Her mental impairment was now more apparent and making me uncomfortable. I suggested she move outside to the front porch. She could have a cigarette while I typed a receipt for her and an agreement. To be honest I felt uncomfortable being alone with her. I made sure the door was open and my secretary was within earshot until Sheryl made it to the front porch.

The contract acknowledged that the prints and negatives would remain her property. I would only keep the three prints and the corresponding negatives in my possession until I was done with them, or until she requested them back. She gave me her express permission to show them to people who might be able to identify the images and offer suggestions. I promised to not publish them without her prior written permission.

I said, "Keep your other prints and negatives someplace safe. I'll see what I can come up with. Don't worry. This will be our secret. I promise to call you when I have any news."

Just then my law clerk returned, thank God! Sheryl was beginning to grow agitated again.

I returned her pictures and the negatives less one strip in the same envelope. I also gave her a copy of the agreement she signed. I was happy to see that she read it. She said she had no questions.

"Sheryl, try to get some more pictures."

"Yes, I will." She lit another cigarette hopped in the cab of her truck and drove off.

I had a nagging suspicion that my phone would ring twenty times a day with alien sightings over Bennington. Sheryl had the potential to become a pest and a genuine problem. I was beginning to think this had been a huge mistake.

Fortunately, I was wrong! She did not turn into a pest. In fact, I never took another call from her! As it turned out I'd never see the woman again.

Over the next few weeks I showed the dark picture to a few friends. They all just shrugged their shoulders. I showed acquaintances from all walks of life and from a variety of backgrounds. It was just an interesting photograph, somewhat out of focus.

I never let on that the object in the photograph might be alien in origin. I just presented it in an offhand way and asked what they thought was captured in the picture.

A few people were sure it was a train. A few were dismissive immediately and made comments ranging from, "that's an out-of-focus Christmas tree" to sillier opinions not worth mentioning.

But a faculty member from Michigan State University looked at the photograph for me and showed a keen interest. "Where'd you get this?" he asked.

I explained, "The photograph belongs to a client. It just caught my attention because it looks like something sitting on the railroad tracks."

I asked him to compare the daylight and nighttime photographs side-by-side. Like me, he recognized the tower immediately as a point of reference.

After five full minutes he concluded, "That is most likely a train. But the semicircular shape of the object and the lights make me think not. Also, I don't know what could be causing the smoke? There are no steam locomotives operating anymore, at least not around here."

He was about to hand the picture back when he asked, "Let me have another look, may I?"

I was grateful for his interest, "Absolutely, I'm curious and your opinion is appreciated."

He explained, "In the photograph the lights are pointed in the direction of the photographer and not nearly bright enough to be the headlamp. The train's headlamp should be pointed ahead of the train illuminating the track ahead. But nothing on the track in front or back of this thing is lit-up."

I was quick with a compliment, "Good observation professor, good eye!" It was a detail that no one, including myself had picked up on! As far as I was concerned that eliminated the possibility that the object was a train.

Before he left he suggested, "Call my buddy Manuel. He just retired from the railroad after something like forty years. Tell him Curtis gave you his number. I bet he can tell you right off the bat if that's a train or not."

He pulled out his wallet and sorted through a few business cards and found the phone number for me. I jotted it down and thanked him.

Feeling guilty, I admitted that I was allowing my experiences and bias to turn this into an obsession. I reminded myself that I was self-employed. Every hour I wasted chasing Sheryl's spaceship was an hour I could use to generate income or time I could spend with my kids. Whatever Manuel might have to say about Sheryl's photograph this would be my final effort.

I called Manuel that afternoon. He answered my call on the fifth ring, "Hello this is Manny."

I said, "Manuel you don't know me. I'm a friend of Professor Curtis from the university. He gave me your number and said you could maybe help me out. I have a question about a photograph of a train. He tells me you're the guy that can identify the train for us. Could you help me out and just look at it for me? Your professional opinion would be appreciated?"

He was friendly, even chipper, "Sure I love old trains. I'd be happy to help you out, and please, call me Manny."

I didn't take the time to explain that it wasn't a picture of an old locomotive. We chatted for a few minutes. Manny lived about a half-hour drive from my office. Rather than driving to my office and risking entanglement in downtown traffic he suggested we meet at a local restaurant located about halfway to downtown.

He didn't want to risk being caught in the notorious downtown rush hour. I didn't blame him. We agreed to meet at 2:00 on Wednesday of the following week.

I called Sheryl to let her know about the meeting. I wanted her to know I had an expert to look at her prints. But no one answered, and I had no way to leave her a message, as her mailbox was full. I didn't give it much thought at the time. I had her permission anyway, but I wanted her to be in the loop. I had promised that I'd keep her informed. I would send her a letter.

I arrived at 2:00 sharp. The lunch crowd had thinned out by then. Manny was easy to spot. He's a very large man who wore a distinctive railroad cap. He was already comfortably planted in a booth with coffee in front of him. He told me he had just ordered lunch. I sat across from him and followed his lead looking over the menu. We both had a hamburger, and Manny began talking about is favorite topic. Trains.

Before our lunch arrived, Manny gave me a brief rundown of his experience with the railroad. He was certainly qualified to express an expert opinion. This is a man who loved the railroad.

Our lunch arrived just as I pulled out the two photographs and the negatives. Manny was eager to look them over. But he was visibly disappointed I didn't have a photograph of an old locomotive. But, he was still interested. His evaluation took just a couple minutes.

"First this is not a modern diesel engine or any other kind. This isn't a train," Manny said with confidence.

"If it's not a train what else could be on the tracks Manny?" I asked.

He said, "This is nothing I'm familiar with. If it runs on rails in the United States or Canada I could identify it even with the poor lighting condition. I think … is this thing moving?"

I asked, "So, you think it's in motion Manny?"

"Yeah, the way this gray part is blurred it looks like something in motion. The cloud of steam is stationary. It looks like it's moving to me."

"I see what you mean Manny. So, is it moving to the left or to the right in the photograph?"

Manny took a break to stare at the photo for a few more seconds and finish his coffee in a final gulp.

"Neither. I don't know many things that travel up and down other than helicopters," Manny let out a nervous chuckle. But he looked disturbed.

"I need to know where the shot was taken Mr. Lovelace. This is a danger to people and property. If this is happening as frequently as she says I need to let a yard agent know. Can I get an address and a copy of your print?"

"Sorry, these belong to my client. I can't lend you these or disclose the location either without her permission. She took these in her backyard Manny. The tracks are still in use. Whatever this thing is it shows up about once a month between 3:00 and 4:00 in the morning and scares the hell out of her."

That peaked Manny's interest. He asked, "Has your client ever seen this thing move?"

"I don't know? I never thought to ask Manny," I said, feeling a little dumb for not asking the obvious.

Many asked, "If your client thinks this is a train did she call the railroad and complain?"

"Manny, my client has some limitations. She thinks somehow her neighbors are in control of the whole thing."

"Now I see." Manny got my point.

I said, "Thanks Manny. I can see it could be a hazard to railroad traffic."

"Yeah, if it sits on the tracks she should notify the railroad," Many added.

Manny took off his cap and scratched his bald head. He mumbled, "Uh huh … what could travel straight up and down, Mr. Lovelace?"

I said, "I don't know. Do you have any ideas that you'd care to share with me Manny?" Manny knew more than he was telling me. My intuition told me Manny has had an experience or two of his own.

He lowered his voice, "You'll think this is crazy but when I used to drive freight I was crossing the New Mexico desert in 1959. About midnight, straight ahead of me I saw what I thought was a car sitting on the track a mile ahead. I hit my whistle hard and flashed my lights."

"So, what happened?" I asked.

"It shined a very bright spotlight back at me for a second or maybe two…. Then it bolted straight into the air like a bullet. It was faster than any damn helicopter. It was something out of this world I'll tell you that!"

"Manny trust me. I don't doubt one word of it," I said. I believed him. Manny knew I believed him.

I put Sheryl's photographs and negatives back in the envelope and put them in my breast pocket. I picked up the tab for lunch and promised Manny I'd get back to him as soon as I had my client's permission to disclose the location. He understood the privacy issue.

We walked out together toward our respective cars. I shook his hand again. He urged me to try to get in touch with my client, so the matter could be investigated. I headed back to the office.

I called Sheryl to let her know what I discovered, which wasn't much. But it was the end for me. I was about to hang up when a young woman answered the phone.

In a businesslike tone a woman answered, "Hello. Foster residence who's calling please?"

I said, "My name is Terry Lovelace. Is Sheryl available?"

"No, I'm sorry can I ask what this is about?" she said.

I introduced myself and she told me she was Sheryl's niece Cindy. She recognized my name from conversations with her aunt and a business card on the refrigerator. Cindy explained that her Aunt Sheryl's health had deteriorated swiftly and considerably.

Cindy said, "My aunt lost her mind the poor thing. She always treated me like a daughter."

"I am so sorry. Your aunt was a very kind lady and I agree. A bit of a lost soul. She spoke very highly of you," I said.

"Thank you, Mr. Lovelace," she said.

Sheryl's family was there to put her things in order. An auction was scheduled for the following weekend. Sheryl had been moved to an assisted living facility. Cindy told me she was her aunt's personal representative and had power of attorney.

"I'm so sorry to hear all this," I told her.

"If you're calling about a bill you'll need to get in line," she said.

I explained, "No I just have a couple photographs that belong to her."

"You're the lawyer that suggested she should set up a camera?" she asked.

I admitted, "Yes, that was my idea Cindy, I thought it might help and didn't think it could cause any harm."

"How much did you charge her for that?" She was blunt. Obviously, she was protective of her aunt. I explained that I didn't charge her. I added, "Cindy I asked your Aunt Sheryl to see her doctor."

"That's alright then Mr. Lovelace. Anything else?" she asked.

I asked Cindy, "I have her photographs and negatives she left with me. Would you like me to mail them to your attention?"

"No whatever photographs you have you can just keep. Maybe the next time I make it downtown I'll stop by and pick them up. Aunt Sheryl had the habit of holding onto things lots of things. We have enough to deal with already."

I told her I understood and said, "I'll keep the photographs just in case you decide to swing by and pick them up." We both knew she never would.

I hung up and directed my energies to cases that needed my attention. Cases that paid the bills.

The photographs were secured in my locked desk drawer. They could sit there until Cindy showed up or until someone who knew more about trains than Manny came along. Meanwhile they served as a good reminder just how precious time was. I rolled up my sleeves and dove back into my work.

A few months later I arrived at work early, about 7:00 AM. I could hear the siren of my alarm system wailing before I'm even out of my car. Unfortunately, the alarm system I bought was a cheap one. It didn't automatically dial the police when triggered. It just let out an ear-piercing siren designed to draw attention. My building was surrounded by offices that were vacant after 6:00 PM so a break-in wouldn't draw attention if it happened in the middle of the night.

The front door to the office was wide open. It looked like it was opened with a key, so I wouldn't need to replace a doorframe. Just a few new locks. I switched off the alarm and dialed 911.

The older downtown section near the courthouse was an area in decline. Over the years, crime had become a worsening problem. It was safe during daylight hours. But at night the downtown was a different world. My secretary joined me on the porch and we waited for the police to arrive.

It was after 10:00 AM before police allowed us back into the building. I began assembling an inventory of what was missing. My secretary and law clerk began working the phones to cancel my appointments and reschedule court matters set for that morning.

Of course, the first thing I checked was the office safe. Either they couldn't open it or just didn't bother. Luckily no important documents were missing. They looted every desk drawer looking for anything of value. Evidently there wasn't a lot of value in hot office supplies.

They had rummaged around and found a couple bucks and a few parking meter tokens. Aside from a twenty-dollar bill I always kept in my drawer, nothing appeared to be missing from my desk at least. I even checked for the envelope with Sheryl's photographs. They were right where I placed them.

An antique set of justice scales worth about $150 were missing. None of the computers were missing. That was our good fortune. Nothing of real value was lost.

Probably using a crowbar or similar tool, they pried open a few desks, mine included. I always kept it locked. There was no damage to the front doorframe. All in all, we fared better than some.

An officer on the scene told me, "Break-ins are common. It's a little unusual to break into a law office but it happens. They look for anything they can sell for drugs. Laptops and cameras are hot items. Of course, they break into desks to look for cash or handguns. I'd suggest an upgrade to your alarm system and replace your locks."

"Good advice, thanks." We cleaned up and I filed an insurance claim. We just moved on.

A year or so later I had a divorce client who was very concerned about losing his collection of toy trains. It was an ugly divorce as most are. His soon to be ex-wife wanted half the value of his toy train collection. Of all the things acquired during the marriage, including a daughter, his biggest concern was his toy train collection.

He asked, "She can't take my trains, can she?"

I told him the bad news, "She can claim one-half interest in the toy trains or their value. That doesn't count the trains you owned before you married her."

He was quick to correct me. They were "model trains" not toys. "These are precision made miniatures that run on electric track. They're made by craftsmen in Germany mostly."

He boasted that he recently bought a single locomotive for $400 and congratulated himself for negotiating such a shrewd deal.

Every man has his toys—boats, motorcycles, golf clubs, guns, and fishing equipment. Of course, others just drank.

I explained a sensitive point, "For negotiating your divorce settlement, the less value they have the better. So, when I refer to them as *toy trains* in your paperwork, don't be offended. Giving up half of less is better than half of more."

He understood.

I was forever amazed at the things men accumulate. Grown men should put their spare cash into their 401k, which they had neglected to fund for twenty years. Toy trains were more fun than numbers on a piece of paper.

While we were on the topic of trains, Sheryl's photographs came to mind. I asked, "Could you look at a picture of a train and tell me what we're looking at?"

He said, "Sure, I'd be happy to. Let's see what you got?"

I opened my desk drawer to grab Sheryl's pictures. Reaching into the back of the drawer my fingers grabbed the envelope. It was exactly where it was supposed to be. I'd not touched them since my lunch with Manny months before the burglary.

As soon as I picked up the manila envelope I knew immediately it was too light. I remembered after the burglary I checked to make sure the envelope was still in my drawer. The envelope was there but I neglected to open it to check on the pictures and the negative!

If Cindy had stopped by to pick them up no one from my office would have pulled them out of my drawer without my permission. My desk drawer was off limits and anything that goes out the door required a signed receipt. I'd check with everyone just to be sure. But of course, no one had.

I was dumbfounded! They were gone! The photographs and the negatives were all missing from the envelope! Occasionally things slipped my mind. But handling a client's property was on a different level than misplacing my keys. Clients' property was treated like gold. It's called a fiduciary duty. I wondered what possible value could they have to anyone?

Shutting my desk drawer, I politely said, "Thanks anyway. They're probably in my safe downstairs." We moved along, and I finished his business.

As soon as we were done I ran downstairs and opened my safe. They were not there. Of course, they were not there! I knew where I kept them. They were locked in my desk drawer. I had the only key on my key ring with a duplicate set safely at home.

I distinctly recalled bringing them back after meeting with Manny and putting them away. But now they were gone.

The entire incident was unnerving. But I'm sure there was a simple explanation.

Black Diamond

It's a fact that UFOs love to visit nuclear installations of all kinds, military and civilian alike. Not only ours. They visit the Russians and the Chinese too. It's widely known and talked about between friends over a beer in backyards at barbeques and on fishing trips.

It's also a fact our military pilots know. They live and work in a culture of silence about the UFO topic. It's the same with commercial airline pilots. Filing a UFO report is career suicide in the United States.

In many other countries it's not that way. Credible UFO reports are accepted and not criticized. In the early 1990s, Belgium experienced hundreds of UFO sightings by civilians in the sky and on radar by multiple members of the Belgian Air Force and commercial pilots. Many of the military pilots gave pursuit but were out-flown on every attempt.

Nuclear power facilities used for generating electricity in the United States are visited by UFOs. According to statistics cited by Wikipedia, there are currently 99 nuclear power facilities operating in the United States. Seventy-four of them have reported multiple UFO sightings.

Four months after I graduated from high school, I enlisted in the United States Air Force. It was 1973, the draft was over, and the Vietnam War was grinding down.

I wasn't looking for a military career and I had no intention of flying aircraft. My parents lacked the financial ability to pay for a college education. So, I enlisted to serve my country for six years in exchange for the education benefits provided by the GI Bill. I wanted for a college education. There was no real patriotic motivation.

I was trained as an EMT and medic. After completing basic training, I had six months of technical training at Shepard Air Force Base in Texas. I was then permanently assigned to Whiteman Air Force Base or WAFB, south east of Kansas City. My education included courses in emergency medicine through the University of Missouri to become credentialed as a paramedic. I drove an ambulance and rendered emergency care to victims of injury or life-threatening illness.

WAFB was a SAC or Strategic Air Command base. It was armed with offensive nuclear weapons. Can there be any other kind? I suppose the threat of a massive retaliatory strike could be considered a defensive use of nuclear weapons.

There was or is a policy of mutually assured destruction appropriately referred to as MAD. It is intended to deter either side from making a preemptive first strike. So far, so good. I'd rather no one possess a nuclear weapon, but the genie is out of the bottle.

Whiteman was home to a squadron of B52s, armed with nuclear bombs. It also housed the Minuteman II missile system. These were sixty-foot-long, nuclear-tipped, intercontinental ballistic missiles or ICBMs.

They were inconspicuously situated in hardened underground missile silos. All of them were removed and decommissioned in the

1990s. But in the 1970s there were dozens of silos and launch control facilities.

They were deep underground and dispersed in soybean fields and farmland all over rural western Missouri. By spreading these out over thousands of acres it would be difficult to hit them all before they could launch their own missiles.

Back then the missiles were aimed over the north pole. Right into the heart of the Union of Soviet Socialist Republic or CCCP. This was the height of the cold war.

It was 1975, my coworker was a young senior airman from Flint, Michigan. Tobias or as everyone knew him "Toby." Toby and I were coworkers and friends. We'd been paired together probably because we were the only two guys in the squadron amenable to working the night shift. We began at 11:00 PM and ended our shift at 8:00 AM.

We made a good team. I felt we had each other's back. In an emergency, each of us knew our respective roles. Over time we polished our skills and became good first responders.

On a bitterly cold winter night, we were playing hearts when the crash phone rang. That meant an emergency of some kind. It could be an aircraft emergency or any kind of mishap at one of the missile facilities. It could mean any number of things. None of them good. We dropped our cards in unison. Toby grabbed the phone to get the details while I started up the ambulance to get it warm.

Seconds later, Toby jumped into the passenger's side and we were off with lights blazing. I didn't use our siren. There was no traffic to maneuver at 2:00 AM, not in rural Missouri. Besides it hurt my head.

As usual, I drove, and Toby navigated. I grabbed the microphone and announced that we were in route with an ETA or an estimated time of arrival of "about 18 minutes."

A voice shot back a quick, "10-4."

Toby gave me the details. We were being dispatched to treat and transport an injured missile mechanic. He was performing routine maintenance on a missile when he slipped from a ladder. We had no information as to how far he fell. The only details given were that he was, "conscious and alert."

I said, "Pretty slim facts, eh Toby?"

Toby nodded and fired up our contraband radio with some loud music and we cruised as fast as 8 General Motors cylinders could propel us. It was Toby's turn. So instead of the Rolling Stones it was "Easy" by the Commodores. When you're 21 it's fun. We weren't fighter pilots, but we weren't chained to a typewriter either! Plus, there was the satisfaction first responders feel when they help someone in need. A lot like practicing law. Making a living off the misfortune of others.

We were about six miles away when Toby killed the music. I picked up the mic to update our ETA to five minutes.

As I hung up the microphone, we saw an orange glow on the horizon made by the red flashing lights of emergency vehicles. They were all flashing out of synch and formed an illuminated orange cloud. It was a mix of exhaust fumes from a dozen running vehicles in the bitter cold. It made for an eerie visual effect.

Toby saw the orange cloud and said, "Man, there's some shit going down out there!"

"Yeah Tobe. The only red lights out here should be ours."

A mile from the scene we encountered a roadblock. Two security policemen parked their cars to stop all traffic in either direction. They were inside their cars for warmth.

I'm sure they were supposed to be standing outside. But it was 2:00 AM, and the wind chill outside had to be well below zero. One of the guys backed up and rolled down his window to motion me through.

I rolled my window down and got his attention, "Hey man, what's going down at Kilo-5?"

"Hell! I don't know! We're stuck out here and can't see a goddamn thing. The radio's quiet too!"

I thanked him, and we drove through. We were on-scene a few minutes later.

This was something we'd never seen before. Something must be very wrong to summon a dozen security police vehicles. That meant about thirty guys with M16s. There must be a damn good reason to summon that much firepower. My guess was a motion detector probably tripped by a deer and some newbie second lieutenant decided to react.

Toby had an opinion, "It's an exercise of some kind I bet."

We rolled into a chaotic scene. On the road and the driveway leading into the missile silo were a dozen security police vehicles. They were randomly parked all with their overhead lights flashing red and their engines running.

Men were crouched down outside their cars while others were running around. It was puzzling. All were carrying rifles. Some just stood fixed in place staring at something. It was interestingly disorganized.

"Terry, man this is no exercise," Toby admitted.

"Toby, you read my mind!"

I killed our overheads and drove into the middle of pandemonium looking around. Someone had to be in charge of this mess.

Standing in the middle of the road was a captain in a parka freezing his ass off. He was talking into a handheld radio. With his free hand he directed me to pull over outside the entry gate. Four guys with rifles stood in front of the gate to block any entry. They were suffering from the cold as badly as their captain. They were all stomping their feet to keep their lower extremities from going completely numb.

"Park it here! Stay off the radio and stay inside your vehicle. Your patient is walking and talking but until I authorize it, no one goes in and no one comes out!"

"Yes Captain."

Apparently, he wasn't taking questions at the moment.

I asked, "Toby what the hell is going on?" I rolled up my window and parked the ambulance.

Toby's answer surprised me, "I don't know man, but I'll snoop around!" With total disregard for the captain's order, Toby slipped on his parka and hopped out of the ambulance to have a look-see.

My windows started to ice from the cold. I couldn't see much more than the red glow. Ten minutes passed before an excited Toby opened my door.

"Man, get out!" Toby was a mix of excitement and laughter. "You have got to see this shit! Get out damn it! Come on!"

I grabbed my parka as Toby pulled me out of the ambulance by my shirtsleeve. Looking around the first thing I saw was about 25 security policemen. They were mostly crouched down beside their cars and others were running around seemingly without direction. They were all holding rifles and most of them were staring up at something.

Toby was laughing, "Man, you ain't never seen no shit like this!"

I managed to get my parka zipped up. Then I saw the captain again. He was still standing in the same place. Right in the middle of the roadway. He still held his two-way radio in one hand. But now he held a pistol in the other hand.

The captain's attention was focused on something over the silo. With his head tilted back, he was staring straight up with his mouth wide open. His breath was billowing out steam in the 12-degree temperature. As he inhaled and exhaled he reminded me of a locomotive.

Tilting back my head I saw what created all the confusion! A black diamond-shaped object was sitting in mid-air over top of the missile silo!

"Ain't that some shit!" Toby added with enthusiasm.

All I could say was, "Toby that's some really freaky shit." I couldn't believe my eyes! I was mesmerized by the sight. It was a little bigger than a full-size van. It sat motionless in the sky 50-feet above the Kilo-5 silo. It was diamond shaped and jet black. Spotlights from a half-dozen security police cars had it lit up. It had a matte surface that was nonreflective.

I strained my eyes looking for wires. My mind was having trouble processing this thing defying gravity. We looked for engines or propeller. We watched it for 10 minutes. It was one of the most amazing things I've ever seen, and it happened in a heartbeat!

Toby had to ask, "So what is it Terry?"

"I don't have a fucking clue Tobe," was my honest answer.

I couldn't take my eyes off the damned thing afraid that sooner or later something had to happen, and I didn't want to miss it!

Everyone there must have had the same idea.

Without warning it took off! It was headed north accelerating at 100+ miles an hour or more from a dead stop. It just shot off! It was out of sight less than a single second. We all stood in silence for a minute before snapping back into the moment.

The captain walked over to me smiling and wide-eyed. He wasn't upset that we had disobeyed his order and left our ambulance. He looked at me as if to ask, "Did you see what I saw?"

For a minute he had put aside his rank. We were two human beings sharing an extraordinary event.

Security policemen and the captain just stared at the hole in space where the thing disappeared. Toby and I stood in the roadway with the captain. We all had our eyes locked on the eastern horizon where it had vanished. Then we were back into reality and into our respective rolls.

Speaking with authority now the captain said, "I'll get the gate!" He ordered the four freezing airmen to open it for us.

The captain said, "Your man is sitting in the shack. You're clear to go fetch him and head back. You can give the doc a status report and your ETA but otherwise stay off the radio. No radio chatter and write up a clean report. Do you understand me sergeant?"

"Yes sir, understood!" I put it in gear.

We drove in and retrieved our patient. He'd broken his ankle when he fell inside the silo. The silo is seventy-feet deep to accommodate the sixty-foot ICBM, so his buddies had to carry him topside. The poor guy. He knew there was something big going on and he was ordered to not move until we arrived.

So, there he sat. He had his leg propped-up on a trashcan while all hell broke loose outside. There were no windows in the shack. He kept asking us, "What was it! What's going on? What'd I miss? You guys got to tell me what you saw! Come on!"

Toby was quick to accommodate, "Man you had to see it to believe it!"

I don't think it helped much.

So, we both enthusiastically told him our version of what we saw. Our stories were identical. It's hard to imagine his frustration at missing a once in a lifetime event happening just outside. While he's stuck inside a guard shack with his leg on a trashcan. He didn't talk about his broken ankle. He just kept asking us questions.

On our ride back to the hospital, a dozen or more helicopters flew past headed for Kilo-5 as we headed in the opposite direction. They had missed the party and the three of us asked each other, "what the hell?" We all wondered why they hadn't been on the scene long before us?

That has me stumped to this day. They were fast enough to have beaten the security police to the scene. I don't get it. The answer must have been above my pay-grade.

It was a very quick ride back to the hospital. A doctor and a nurse were waiting for us. Our patient was strapped to a backboard with his neck immobilized and his ankle splinted. It sounds like overkill but without knowing how far he fell or how he landed it was the correct procedure. We gave them a quick synopsis of what happened to him and what we had done. They took him away and we put our ambulance back together before completing our report.

Our commanding officer was waiting for us. Our CO really was a good guy. We placed officers into two classes. Those who treated enlisted men and women as inferior beings and those who were the good guys, or good women. Our CO was a good guy.

As soon as we had our ambulance restocked and ready to be refueled, he asked us to follow him to his office down the hallway. We knew what he wanted. He missed the party too and wanted an experience by proxy. He shut the door behind us and asked us to pull up a chair.

The first thing he asked was whether we'd documented what we saw in our report. Of course not. Our report was limited strictly to the facts regarding our patient and his treatment and transportation. That was kind of a no-brainer. He asked to review our reports before we filed them. After a careful reading he took a black felt-tipped marker and obliterated the times cited in our report except for my departure time. He then took our report to his copy machine and made two copies. Without explanation, he ordered us to file the photocopies. He slid the originals in his top desk drawer.

With that formality out of the way he asked, "Now boys, what the hell happened out there?" He was fascinated. We couldn't tell him enough details. After we completed telling him everything, he asked each of us to draw what we'd seen.

We both finished in about ten minutes. Our drawings matched up pretty well. Because Toby had counted the panels on the side of the diamond it was easier to recreate on paper. He studied our drawings for 10 minutes before he slid both into his desk drawer, along with our report, and locked it.

I spoke up, "Sir, may I ask, what was that thing? How did it fly without wings or engines?"

He put on his officer-face and said, "Guys that was an experimental helicopter. Okay?

"Yes sir. I understand!" Toby and I spoke in unison.

His face betrayed him. He didn't have the slightest idea either.

"Guys, it's probably a prototype of some sort. So, for that reason it's secret, understand?"

"Yes sir!" Again, we spoke in unison.

Then he warned us, "That means no talking to anyone. Just forget about it, okay? Finish up your shift and go home. I know you are both smart guys so don't screw up and run your mouths. I mean it. No talking or it could mean trouble."

Of course, we couldn't wait to do just that! We didn't call the press or talk about it with anyone outside our small circle of trusted friends. But we ran our mouths as fast as any auctioneer.

On our way out of the building we passed our poor patient still in the treatment room. A security police lieutenant and two enlisted police officers were busy interrogating the poor guy. We were happy albeit a bit surprised that no one from security police debriefed us.

I said, "Hey Toby! The guy they picked to interrogate was the only guy out there that didn't see shit!"

That was good for a laugh. I was grateful we didn't have to sit down with the cops and tell the same story a third or fourth time.

It was 7:00 AM and we went to Toby's house to have a cold beer and conduct our own debriefing. When you work the nightshift a beer at 7:00 in the morning tastes pretty good.

Toby's wife, Tammy, made us sandwiches and we sat down to discuss the evening. Of course, Tammy wanted to hear every detail.

We filled her in on everything that happened after the crash-phone rang.

I asked Toby, "So, was that thing Soviet made or was it one of ours?"

Toby speculated, "Terry man, no way that thing was made by us. That was Soviet made I'd bet!"

I half agreed, "Toby that thing was either made by the United States or by the Soviet Union. The CO said it was an experimental helicopter, but he might as well winked-an-eye when he said it!"

Toby agreed, "How would he know? He didn't see shit. That was no damn helicopter."

I just nodded in agreement.

Tammy wanted us to draw the thing we saw. Toby had a good eye for detail. I copied his drawing, so I could show it to Sheila when I got home.

By 10:00 AM, I was at home telling Sheila the whole story and showing her my drawing. I considered myself to be an expert on extraterrestrial aircraft! This thing was shaped like a diamond and not a flying saucer. For that reason alone, I believed it was a manmade terrestrial object. But the technology was way ahead of anything I'd ever seen. Maybe the CO was right, and it was a prototype aircraft out for a cruise.

That was the third strange thing I'd seen in the sky! But this was no flying saucer. What I didn't know was that it wouldn't end with Kilo-5. Oh, there was more to come.

Two years flew by. It was 1977 and the Kilo-5 incident was ancient history. Toby and I were still manning our ambulance in the Whiteman AFB Emergency Room. We were still working the night shift and watching the sky. I was taking evening classes when available and we both were counting off the months until we'd be civilians again.

Working with someone you can get along with makes life easier. Our wives were friends as well. We socialized and got together every week or so for a barbeque or to play cards. Toby and Tammy had had a second child by this time.

We were on duty one cold morning around 4:00 AM when Toby called me outside. "Come see this, hurry up will ya!"

Throwing on my parka I went outside to see whatever had Toby in a hissy fit. He sat in a lawn chair in twenty-degree weather gazing at the stars and munching a tuna salad sandwich. Pulling up my lawn chair I asked him, "So what's up?"

Pointing with half his sandwich, Toby said, "Look at the North Star." All the while his eyes were glued to the night sky.

I said, "Okay I see it," wishing I'd brought the binoculars I kept in my desk drawer.

Toby guided my sight, "Now look halfway between the North Star and the eastern horizon just slightly to your left. See it?"

I was impressed! I said, "Hell yes! How could I not?" Fully expecting an answer, I asked, "What on earth is that thing Toby?" I was torn between staying or running back inside to get my binoculars. I opted to stay.

This night Toby had spotted a glowing orb in the eastern sky. It was relatively big too. It was about the size and brilliance of the North Star but shaped like a globe! It looked like a miniaturized moon. It did not twinkle like a star and it was larger than a planet. It was unquestionably round and slowly traversing the night sky.

Toby said, "Terry man, I know satellites, and I know aircraft, but this is a new one on me. It's got to be one big-ass satellite!"

We watched it in silence. It traveled about ten seconds more before it blinked out. As if someone had flipped the switch, it vanished! Show over. We chalked-it up to just another weird thing in the sky and never gave it a second thought.

I didn't voice it at the time, but the thing made me a bit uneasy for some reason. I didn't sleep well for a couple nights but didn't make any connection.

It's true. If you watch the sky often from time to time, you'll see things that are just unusual. This is especially true if you're away from the lights of an urban area. "Light pollution" was the phrase Toby used to describe it. In the backwoods of rural Missouri on a cloudless night the sky was brilliantly lit with billions of stars.

I remember getting excited once when I saw a star moving across the sky one night. Toby was quick with an explanation. It was just a satellite. There weren't a lot of satellites in the air in 1977. But Toby knew most of them at least the ones that crossed our path.

Sometimes he could even predict when they'd make an appearance. Often, we bet it was the Russians watching us watch them. But this was not a satellite, at least not like any of the things we'd seen before.

Star-watching was Toby's hobby and hopefully his career one day. It gave him a good reason to prefer the night shift. He was an amateur astronomer and a skilled mathematician. He lived to watch the night sky. He found beauty in the symmetry of math the way I found it in works of art or good music.

Central Missouri State University ran a satellite campus on base. They offered a handful of classes in their evening division that ran from 6:00 PM to 9:00 PM five nights a week.

Unfortunately for Toby there were only two classes offered that he could possibly transfer to the University of Michigan. Both were physics classes. Toby had already taken and aced them both.

Initially, I didn't get the connection between arithmetic and astronomy. Toby quickly educated me. Evidently math and arithmetic are different subjects too. It was the price I'd pay for sleeping through math class.

Soon I was back in the building that night. Back inside where it was warm. Toby eventually called it quits and came back inside too. Besides, it was time to play hearts until 5:00 AM. We kept a schedule.

Let's Go Camping!

Several uneventful months passed. One spring morning we had just finished up our paperwork from a longer than usual night shift when Toby said, "Hey I got an idea. Let's go camping!"

I asked, "What the hell did you say?"

Toby said, "What would you think about taking a camping trip? You bring your camera and I'll bring my decent binoculars."

I shook my head with disapproval.

Toby clarified; he said, "Not now. I mean when the weather warms up a little?"

"Camping?" I asked. "I don't know the first thing about that kind of stuff. We're city-boys Toby."

Toby had done some homework on the subject. He said, "Just listen, there's a very cool national park just a few hours south of here. Warm weather's still a few months down the road. Just think about it."

I promised I'd give it some thought. Toby dropped the subject and we returned to our normal routine. A couple days later I noticed it was on my mind especially in the early morning hours when I was going to sleep.

I thought about the camping trip idea. I gave it a lot of consideration. Over the span of forty-eight hours it became an obsessive thought. I wondered what our wives would think of the idea. I doubted they'd embrace the idea of roughing it at a campground in a state park somewhere. It also occurred to me that in addition to the four of us we'd also have Toby's two toddlers in tow. It just wasn't practical.

I could think of other vacations we could take and include our wives. We could drive to Kansas City, hit the museum there or maybe enjoy a nice restaurant. There were plenty of things to do. The only problem… those activities required money. But despite the economic advantages, I was leaning toward nixing the camping idea.

I said, "Toby I just don't think our wives would enjoy themselves."

Toby rolled his eyes, "Man, you totally misunderstood me. I never meant we'd take the old ladies! I thought we'd go. Just us. Spend a couple nights in the wilderness. Let's see how we like it. Then if we enjoy ourselves we can take them along on our next trip. Once we've worked out all the bugs. It's a vacation on the cheap."

I was quick with a reply, "Work the bugs out you say? Oh, yeah there's bugs alright. Mosquitos and ticks are all over the place. Plus leaving our wives at home alone with your two kids? There's no way they'd ever go along with that idea Toby."

Toby persisted. He said, "You dig nature photography. You might never be this close again to a big nature preserve. I like watching the stars. There's a park just across the Arkansas border called Devils Den. It would give you plenty of scenery and wildlife to photograph. There are bluffs where I could watch the stars from a high point with zero light pollution."

I said, "But the bugs Toby, you know how brutal the mosquitos are."

"Man, that's why we have military strength insect repellent and sunscreen stuff. We work a lot of hours and we're entitled to a little R&R. It's not like we're out on fishing trips every weekend. We don't bowl or play golf like the other guys in the squadron."

I admitted, "You're right, you got me there Tobe."

Toby couldn't help but gloat when he won an argument with me. He said, "Damn right man, the outdoors would be a real change! We could leave the wives at home. I was only thinking of two nights tops. Other than gas, it wouldn't break the bank. I think they'd be okay with it. Just think about it."

"I'll give it more thought," I said. He made some very good points. That was the end of the camping idea for a while. It turned out to be a very short while.

Over the next week, I picked up on the camping idea. I could see the upside to a short getaway. We both had a four-day weekend in June. Maybe we could spend a night or two away. It might do us good to have some R&R.

There was another point worth mentioning. I had a new 35mm camera and some lenses I was hot to try out. Photography on a nuclear base was frowned upon. If I wanted to use the equipment, I needed to leave the base.

Toby knew me well. I did enjoy photographing wildlife. We could pitch a cheap tent and buy a couple air mattresses. Everything else we either already had or could borrow. Like Toby said "It's camping. It ain't rocket science and it won't break the bank."

He won me over. I now found myself obsessed with Toby's camping trip proposal. My wife and I discussed it over a breakfast. I was pleasantly surprised that she wasn't against the camping idea! Not completely at least. There were some caveats.

Before going to bed she said, "Let's think about Toby's camping idea. I want to see what Tammy thinks."

"That's reasonable, thank you." I knew that meant yes.

I began to run through it in my mind. There would be plenty of photo-ops with scenery and wildlife. We could pitch a tent and build a campfire to cook over. Being outside in the fresh air sounded appealing. We needed a cooler with some ice, a couple beers and hotdogs. It would be affordable.

The following weekend was our usual BBQ night at Toby's. Naturally the topic of the camping trip came up. Our wives had discussed it and already given us their blessing. They knew that if they didn't agree we'd eventually go anyway.

In the span of two weeks from Toby's initial suggestion this camping trip idea consumed me. It was all I could do to stay focused on the day-to-day grind of work and obligations at home. What had turned an offhand suggestion into a full-blown obsession? The word obsession fails to accurately describe my feelings. As the days ticked off and the camping trip got closer the more excited we became.

Toby confessed to virtually the same obsessive thoughts. Like me, he found it difficult to focus on anything else as well. We both thought it was natural excitement about trying something new. I think it was something more.

Toby and I were known as the academics in the squadron. We would be labeled as nerds today. Toby was a genius at math and would have some scholarship money waiting for him. He hoped to study physics for undergrad and astronomy or cosmology in graduate school.

As academics, we approached the camping trip idea like solving any other problem. With pencil and paper. We first discussed and then compiled a list of essentials. Toby poured over maps from several sources. He ran into a guy with a great map he had laying in his glove box. He gave it to Toby explaining, "I tried fishing. It's not for me."

Toby insisted that we camp at a place called Devils Den adjacent to the Ozark National Forest and Wildlife Preserve near Russellville, Arkansas. I thought it was a little crazy to drive to Arkansas to go camping. Especially since there were dozens of beautiful parks all around us.

But Toby gave a well-rehearsed rebuttal. He said, "Sure there's lots of parks closer but the campgrounds aren't much more than a parking lot in the woods. Where's the fun in that? This is the place to go for wildlife and wilderness scenery! We both want to hike and there are great trails. Just the scenery is worth the drive. Besides isn't the journey part of the adventure?"

I caved, "Alright, okay I got it. I agree!"

Toby would be our navigator for the trip. We already had our four-day weekend in the bag. We had planned to spend two overnights to explore and a full day to relax before returning to work.

We searched the base library for a guidebook on camping. Our sole reference source was a Scouting Manual from 1958.

It turned out to be of no help whatsoever. We would not be tracking deer through the woods. There would be no snaring, trapping, or killing of rabbits or squirrels. Taxidermy skills would not be needed. We had little need for learning to tie various nautical knots. Archery skills were not a priority. Neither of us would be repelling off limestone cliffs. Although, if we'd had the gear I'd been game. We didn't intend to fish. Neither of us had a fishing license or owned a fishing pole. Neither of us hunted.

We scrounged bottles of USAF strength DEET. The infamous Missouri mosquitos could swarm in droves and I'm sure they were no less vicious in Arkansas. There was equatorial strength sunscreen for me. Toby said he didn't need it. We snagged a couple hospital blankets too.

Of course, we had a first-aid kit on the list. We included six gallons of freshwater and a cooler full of ice, beer, soda, beans, and hot dogs seemed adequate. I remembered the bottle opener, a necessity in the 70s. It all went on the list. A kind neighbor lent us a camp lantern and decent hatchet. Everything made the list, including the toilet paper, thanks to my wife.

We had covered all the bases on paper. Unfortunately, our logistics were faulty. We took less care loading for the trip. It was uncharacteristically sloppy for us, especially considering that we inventoried and stocked our ambulance every workday. We planned correctly but failed with the execution. Afterward it felt liked we'd engineered our failure.

Everyone in the squadron knew about our trip. I had checked out a book of Ansel Adams photographs from the base library. I bought a variety of black and white film and boasted I'd bring back Ansel Adams quality photographs of scenery and wildlife. That's a tall order.

As we planned our trip, we took our fair share of ribbing too. Coincidentally a bigfoot had been sighted a week before our trip. A bigfoot-like creature was alleged to have carried away a three-hundred-pound hog and killed the farmer's dog. Supposedly, it now roamed the backwoods of mid-Missouri.

In small farm towns of the heartland, bigfoot sightings made front-page news. Missouri's version of bigfoot was dubbed what else? "MOMO." Short for Missouri Monster in the local press and on radio. It's easy to forget just how many people live in the middle of nowhere. Remote places where nothing of real interest ever happens.

We were the brunt of more than a few MOMO jokes and pranks. Someone had replaced the label on a can of air freshener with a hand-drawn label that read, "MOMO Repellent Extra Strength." It was packed into our bag of gear. I thought it was a pretty good prank.

When asked about our agenda, it was hiking and wildlife photography for me. For Toby, it was hiking and star gazing with an unhindered view of the universe.

We brushed off the jokes and sojourned on. We envisioned sitting around a campfire and cooking a meal over the open flames. Star gazing at night. We'd never been camping before and this had the feel of an adventure for a couple of guys who grew up in the city. It was like being 12 again.

I don't recall watching a movie or television program that might have spawned a sudden interest in the wilderness. Likewise, Toby couldn't trace the genesis of this camping idea. Toby said the idea just, "popped into my head."

We never considered a national park to be dangerous. Decades later, I stumbled across a disturbing story that made me rethink that judgment. In fact, people do disappear from national parks all too often. Lots of people. Most are found, with some of them being remains, but others were never found at all. I discovered the name *Devils Den* was coined by Native Americans who considered the land to be cursed. Local tribes avoid the area to this day.

After what had felt like the longest seven weeks of my life, it was finally June. That meant it was time for our trip to Devils Den! We kissed our wives' goodbye and packed the trunk of my Impala with the gear we had collected.

On a beautiful, muggy Missouri morning we left at 6:00 AM full of coffee and enthusiasm. Enthusiasm is an understatement. We felt like Lewis & Clark about to depart St. Louis to explore the West.

There was the usual line of morning traffic at the gate. Our timing wasn't the greatest. We left the base at shift change. With a dozen cars waiting to exit in front of us we were stuck and inpatient. By half past the hour we were off base and on the open road. As soon as my tires hit the two-lane blacktop headed south, we were on top of the world.

I said, "Toby, you were right man. This was a great idea!"

I envisioned this expedition as just the start of a lifetime filled with family camping trips. We discussed bringing our wives and Toby's kids on the next trip. This would be the inaugural trip of what I thought would become an established family tradition.

I planned to begin looking at used vans or campers for sale as soon as we got back! It sounds extreme, but I could best describe our mood as euphoric. Who could have imagined this would be the last camping trip of my life? It would be the last vacation in Toby's life.

I manned the steering wheel and Toby navigated. His responsibilities were to control the radio and dispense soda and sandwiches packed courtesy of our wives. I drove as fast as I thought safe to avoid an encounter with some small-town sheriff. There were stories galore about young airmen from the base being mistreated by small town sheriffs. Even worse were the stories of airmen getting badly roughed-up in small-town taverns by local farm boys. I guess they considered us competition for the limited supply of available women. We'd be visiting no taverns or competing for anyone's homegrown girl.

From the beginning we agreed to steer clear of the park's campsite. While it provided electricity and restrooms, it was packed with children and other undesirables. I had heard that campgrounds were overrun with hippy types playing their guitars and singing campfire songs. Turning their demon-seed children loose to run amuck with firecrackers and playing pranks on the unwary.

It's odd, all the typical fun things to do while camping we chose to avoid! For some reason, with our limited exposure to the outdoors, we sought the wilderness. I had never been camping in my life, but I felt like a seasoned outdoorsman. Like Toby said, "It ain't rocket science."

I agreed with Toby that it made sense to find high terrain for our campsite. Something high with a panoramic view of streams and woodlands below. I had promised Ansel Adams-grade photography to our friends at the hospital including our commanding officer. I began daydreaming about taking some breathtaking photographs. I bought a variety of black and white 35mm film to try, including a couple rolls of ultraviolet film.

In the middle of a mental image of soaring eagles against a panoramic sky, a thought flashed through my mind. Did I leave my camera bag on the kitchen counter? We had already been on the road for three hours. I racked my brain going over my actions loading the car.

"Shit Toby! I left my goddamn camera in the kitchen," I said.

Puzzled he asked, "What did you say?" Toby turned off the music.

"Damn it Tobe! I was so eager to get on the road … No, this just can't be!" I pounded the steering wheel with my fist!

How could I forget the goddamn camera? It made no sense. Then a glimmer of hope. I thought it might be in the trunk. I said, "Toby maybe it got thrown in the trunk with the cooler!"

Toby piped-up quickly, "Man, pull this thing over now! Let's check the trunk. I bet your camera is back there." He was already rummaging around the back seat. We were on a state highway but there was no place to safely pull over. Just a very narrow shoulder separated the asphalt from rocks and an incline. But we'd be quick. I was hoping like hell it would be there. Anyone who's ever lost their car keys knows the feeling.

As soon as the car stopped, we both hopped out. I turned the key and opened the trunk. It was loaded with crap tossed in with haste. Toby began unloading the trunk tossing everything into a random pile. He pulled out blankets air mattresses and the cooler.

Lastly, he pulled out the tent. Everything was dumped by the side of the highway. We combed through everything. But there was no reward. It wasn't in the backseat either. There simply was no camera to find. It was on my kitchen counter and that was three hours north of where we sat. That would mean a six-hour round trip to retrieve it. Six hours just to get to where we were sitting.

There would be no spectacular Ansel Adams-style photography on this trip. No sunsets or nature scenes. Forgetting my camera would be just the first of many disappointments to come. I decided to be a grown-up and roll with it. There was no one to be angry with but myself. I had to accept it and salvage a nice camping trip.

Toby tried to cheer me, he said, "Man those damn eagles will still be there! That forest ain't going anyplace!"

"You're right, thanks Toby. We'll make this a trip to reconnoiter."

My old car had no air conditioning, so we cruised with the windows down and the stereo as loud as possible just short of distortion. After an hour, the little towns grew smaller and further apart. There was an abrupt change in the terrain. We were entering the Ozark Mountains. There were fewer cornfields and more stretches of thick virgin forest on rolling hills.

FM radio was not standard in American cars of the 1960s. On the AM band there were just a couple of Spanish stations left. We caught the farm report quoting prices for sowbellies. Toby said, "Sowbellies! They sell just the bellies? That conjured up some ugly mental imagery. There was the occasional radio preacher or two with their pessimistic prophecies and pleas for money. We listened to accordion music from somewhere drift in and out.

Trying to lift my sour mood, Toby did his best imitation of a radio preacher. It cracked me up and helped lift my spirits. He was really pretty good. He boasted he'd learned his preaching skills at the First Baptist Church of Flint.

Eventually the radio distortion got so bad that we turned the damn thing off and listened to the hum of the road. I don't think we had much to say. We were focused on the road and anxious to arrive. I pushed the envelope with my speed.

Ten minutes later we stopped at a little country store and gas station to fill up. There was only one pump. The attendant was a pleasant enough guy. He pumped the gas checked our oil and cleaned our windows. That was typical service back in the day. I guess it's why we referred to them as service stations. We went inside the old store to look around. We decided to split a bag of pork rinds and a couple pickled sausages from the gallon jar on the counter. Before "SELL BY" dates became common we relied on sight and smell to choose what was safe. The sausages were questionable but tasty. Luckily neither of us suffered any ill effects.

You could tell by the architecture the place was old. It had high ceilings covered in tin tiles and well-worn wooden flooring. I would guess the building had been around for a century or more. The long wooden counter suggested it had once been a bar or maybe a dry goods store selling farm equipment and animal feed to the locals.

I grabbed a cold six-pack of Fallstaff and dropped our stuff by the register. I politely asked the young lady behind the counter to, "Ring us up and get the gas too please."

The clerk was a depressed looking farm girl. I surmised she ran the register when necessary and read romance novels the rest of her day. She was deep in the middle of a paperback when we arrived. Dozens of books littered her space behind the counter. It was also apparent she visited the pastry shelf a little too often. It felt like we were interrupting her. She rang up our items on a hand crank calculator. She glanced up from her book and back at the adding machine. Without making eye contact she remarked, "You boys ain't from around here, are you?" Classic. The singsong tone in her voice was less than friendly.

Toby failed to grasp that her question was rhetorical. He chimed in with a big smile and answered proudly, "I'm from Flint!"

Startled she switched her gaze over to Toby and looked baffled. I was white, and Toby was black. I honestly think Toby was the first black person she'd ever met.

"Never heard of it," she said, "But I don't get out of the town much." She was now smiling at Toby dreamily. Toby remained oblivious.

"Thanks!" I said and grabbed our bag.

That interrupted her train of thought wherever it was headed. She reverted to an abrupt and dismissive tone, "Ya'll have a good one." She dove back into the fantasy world of her romance novel.

We got into the car and had a good laugh and a cold beer. I told Toby, "Man I think that farm girl had her eye on you."

That got me a mean look only Toby could deliver.

I popped the trunk and threw four beer cans into the cooler. That gave us a can each for the last leg of the trip. We were happy to be back on the road. There was comfort in the fact that we were only an hour or two away from our destination. The afternoon was humid, and the cold beer was refreshing.

In 1977 drunk driving was rightfully a serious offense. But drinking alcohol from an open container was perfectly legal in Missouri. Sipping from an open can of beer in your car was no problem. So long as you were sober in the eyes of the officer and over 21. It was a different time. Toby's job had been to pack two six packs in the cooler for the trip. He left them both in his refrigerator.

We rolled up on a road sign that read, "Welcome to Arkansas! The People Rule!"

Toby cracked me up again, "Hey, didn't that say, *Where the White People Rule?*"

We crossed the Arkansas border and were tired of the long drive and ready to arrive and get camp setup. Soon enough we were turning into Devils Den State Park. As planned, we bypassed the main gate and visitor center that issued camping permits. We managed to skirt the park rangers too. Toby managed to snag a map from a rack of local tourist attractions. Now we had a better idea how to find our way into the wilderness area. The map only took us as far as the entrance of the wildlife preserve.

From this point onward Toby directed me while he drew a map on the back of a bank envelope. The lack of recognizable landmarks made the map a necessity. We passed a sign that said, "No Admittance No Hunting No Fishing."

After a mile or two of twisting roads, the terrain got rougher. Toby directed the way doing his best to keep us on trails and making sure to accurately chart the path as I drove. After we ran out of blacktop the road turned into gravel and the gravel degraded into a rough dirt road. Eventually we had just ruts in the clay to follow. We came to a chain across the road blocking our way. A second metal sign was posted that read, "No Entry, Arkansas Department of Parks and Recreation."

I said, "Damn the trespass!" The chain was locked in a loop and just slid over the opposite post. Toby hopped out of the car and lifted the chain up and over. He let it fall to the ground with a "chink!" We were jubilant. I knew trespassing was unlawful but assumed the worst that could happen would be an ass-chewing by a pissed off park ranger. They could eject us from the park maybe. We intended no harm.

In a few places, the road was beautifully canopied by trees. There were a few shallow streams to cross. This was territory suited for a jeep, not a Chevy Impala. Ever the vigilant navigator, Toby diligently charted our course. We'd need to rely on his map when it became time to backtrack. We never dreamed how valuable Toby's little map would become in a matter of hours.

The grade continued a subtle climb upward. The road took us along a dirt trail high up along limestone bluffs without guardrails. The dangers were apparent. Now I understood the reason for the chain and warning sign. This wasn't a place for amateurs. After an hour of twists and turns our path took us up a sharp hill to the summit of a plateau.

At the summit, we entered a pasture of wildflowers in late bloom. It was a carpet of white and blue. We were awestruck. Neither of us spoke. This was the spot! This had to be the place. It offered the panoramic view of the wilderness just as I imagined. This met our expectation in every detail and we were thrilled. "Nice work!" I said.

Pulling up to a spot backing the woods, we got out of the car and stretched. I popped the trunk and grabbed a gallon of ice water and a couple sandwiches. Leaning against the car we took in the view some more. Again, I cursed leaving my camera behind.

Toby wisely suggested we take time to set up camp now. But I vetoed the idea and suggested we go for a hike now and look around a little instead. Toby didn't like the idea. He was eager to set up camp before exploring. But after some back and forth he relented. I would very soon regret my impulsive foolishness.

We locked the car and put the cooler back in the trunk. I told Toby, "This will keep it safe in case there are black bears in the area." Toby was laughing at me, "Man there ain't no goddamn bears in Arkansas white boy! Momo might get your ass though!" I was fine with poisonous snakes and most other dangers in the wilderness. But I was terrified of bears, even if the odds of an encounter were remote.

Toby intended to get out his little camera. But decided instead to save his film for tomorrow's hike. I grabbed a milk jug of water and we set off exploring.

It was now midafternoon, and we planned to be back by 6:00 PM. That would leave plenty of time to set up camp. It would also give us enough time to gather firewood before sundown.

The scenery was breathtaking. I imagined trappers and traders of early America walking these trails. Before them, Native Americans walked the same. We were walking the trails Neolithic men had taken long before us. It was humbling.

Soon, we lost sight of the meadow behind heavy brush. The trail took many twists and turns. It made me a little uncomfortable, but I had confidence in Toby to help us navigate back to the meadow. After some rough terrain we came to a limestone bluff. Climbing to the top, we were rewarded with an awesome scene. Below us were a couple freshwater creeks that fed into a larger stream. The bluffs were pristine. No litter and no graffiti. The air was fresh. Being in the very best physical condition of my life, I hopped down from the ledge and headed straight for the creek. It became a footrace and Toby was hot on my heels. Toby could outrun me on his worst day. He let me win this day.

I should have brought binoculars and probably a compass too. I was still unnerved by the fact I couldn't spot the meadow through the woods.

"Time for some sunscreen for you," Toby reminded me and tossed it in my direction. I rubbed the lotion liberally onto my arms, the back of my neck and forehead. I wore my cap and never took off my tee shirt.

I was spent from the drive and the hike. We had covered three miles of tough terrain as the crow flies. But we walked probably five miles in total to navigate the trail. I was ready to find a spot to rest. That limestone ledge we had just passed made an ideal place to rest. There was a canopy of tree branches overhead for shade and the stone was cool to the touch. It was comfortable to sit back and enjoy the view. We killed the last of the warm water in our gallon jug and applied some DEET. We chatted a little but mostly we just relaxed.

No sooner than I had gotten comfortable than I began to feel drowsy. I was tired from the long drive and our hike. But I shouldn't have been sleepy. There's a difference between the two.

"Man, this is nice," remarked Toby enjoying the shade and a breeze.

The last thing I remember saying was, "Toby, this is perfect!"

I guess neither of us knew how truly exhausted we really were. I'm sure neither of us thought the other would dare to fall asleep. But we did. At some point both of us dozed off. I was in a deep dreamless sleep.

Suddenly I had Toby kicking me and screaming, "Get up, get your ass up!" I could hear the panic in Toby's voice even before I opened my eyes.

"It's almost sundown! Man, we haven't set up camp or even gathered firewood!" Toby exclaimed.

Rubbing my eyes, I noticed the sun was getting low in the western sky. This was unbelievable! How could we possibly have slept so long? I lost track of time, but I never imagined we could end up this far from our camp this late in the day! We both panicked.

Quickly gathering up our things Toby scampered down the trail ahead of me. He just kept saying, "shit, shit, shit." I had to hustle to keep up with him. I was afraid he'd outdistance me and the two of us would be separated.

When I realized we were panicked, I yelled at Toby, "Stop Toby … stop running."

Toby stopped.

Winded, I said, "Let's both calm down and take a minute." We both took a few deep breaths.

We were determined not to tackle this unexpected and untimely problem in a blind panic. Toby agreed. After a few minutes of scouting the horizon Toby announced with confidence, "this way," and we changed direction.

I cursed myself aloud for failing to bring a lantern or decent flashlight along.

Toby heard me, "What we needed was a damn alarm clock, fool." He was a little more pragmatic.

It went unsaid but both of us were terrified at the idea of spending the night in the forest without the benefit of shelter or fire. A night in the woods without fire and water would be survivable but miserable. It would be the penalty for poor planning.

The trail looked different to me until we reached the creek. Then I knew we'd be okay. I would have chosen a completely different route and probably been lost until the following day. Perhaps worse.

At the point of exhaustion, we reached the crest of the meadow as the sun slipped low on the horizon. The glow from the setting sun lit the way for us as we sprinted the last hundred yards.

I was never so happy to see my old Chevy. We sat on the ground next to the car for few minutes to catch our breath. A few swigs of warm water from the milk jug and it was time to bust-ass. It was shaping up to be a sweltering summer evening.

Without warning, it was as if someone rang a dinner bell for the mosquitoes. We rapidly reapplied a drenching dose of DEET and quickly discussed our options.

I said, "We had plenty of gas left in the car. We could call it quits and head for home?"

Toby vetoed that idea. Even with his map backtracking in the dark without benefit of visible landmarks could worsen our position. Sitting tight was the best option. Besides why not make the best of it?

I agreed. Now we went about frantically putting together a camp. A task we'd only done before in our minds. But like Toby said, "It ain't rocket science."

We were determined to salvage what we could of day #1. If we hustled, we could pull this together and still enjoy a pleasant evening.

With the last bit of daylight fading, I pulled the car around to face the campsite. The headlights would give us enough light to setup a campsite in twilight and hopefully not drain the battery.

Once we had everything unloaded we decided the best course of action was to divide up our tasks. Toby was experienced putting together kids' toys. That meant he was our chief engineer and responsible for assembling the tent and setting things up as needed.

My sole responsibility was to collect enough firewood to get us through our first night. All I needed was the hatchet. As I went to retrieve it, it dawned on me. I'd left it in the garage alongside the camping lantern and a gallon of fuel lent to me by a neighbor.

We were not this inept. It felt like we had unconsciously sabotaged our efforts.

Toby had slipups of his own to deal with. He'd forgotten his good flashlight and he'd forgotten the pot for the canned beans. He'd forgotten the beans! The instant coffee and various other provisions we'd purchased for the trip were left in the trunk of Toby's car.

Toby was wrong. Maybe this was on the order of rocket science. Despite six weeks of planning we were woefully unprepared. It was a testament to our haste to get to the park.

Finding a rusty kitchen knife with a four-inch blade, I tried to make due. It was a pathetic excuse for a machete. I abandoned it quickly in favor of bare hands to gather as much brush as I could carry. I was limited to scrounging bark, twigs, and a few fallen branches. At least it was dry. I kept gathering kindling to the point of exhaustion. I hoped to make up for the lack of quality with quantity.

Toby soon had the tent set up and properly staked. He used a rock as a hammer. Our plan was to use the flat side of the hatchet to stake the tent. We were proud of our tent selection. It had a canvas floor and a mosquito screen with zippered flaps. It slept three and it was cheap. Considering everything we'd left at home we were grateful the tent made its way to the trunk. Sleeping in my car would have added insult to injury.

I stacked the wood about eight-feet away from the tent toward the meadow. I chose an area I designated as the fire pit about ten-feet in front of the tent. When I was done, I killed the lights on the car to preserve the battery and pulled it back so as not to block our view of the meadow. We had set-up camp at the wood line with forest to our back and a view of the entire meadow in front of us.

I stacked about half our wood in the fire pit and held half in reserve. With a single match it went up with a roar. The sobering thought of an accidental forest fire crossed my mind.

The fire was bright enough to light up the campsite. I estimated we had about three hours of fuel to burn if we were lucky. That would have to suffice. Considering how exhausted we were it was agreed that when the fire died out, we'd call it a night.

Despite our long unscheduled nap, we were both worn-out. I distinctly recognized that drowsy feeling creeping over me again. I shook it off and hustled to settle in before the twilight turned into darkness.

Incident at Devils Den

I grabbed the cooler from the trunk and inventoried what we had. Most of the ice had melted. Still the beer was a few degrees below tepid. I busted out a package of hot dogs and a bag of badly smashed buns. I opened a bag of chips and a bag of cookies.

I skewered eight hot dogs and promptly burned all eight over the blazing brushfire I called a campfire. While Toby finished off his details I assembled two plates of food.

We sat down, and Toby stared at his plate with the four black hot dogs. He never said a word. A hot meal was good. It's true that things taste better when cooked over an open flame. Even burnt hotdogs. We inflated our air mattresses and lounged around by the campfire.

The scent of the wood fire was pleasant in the way my grandfather's pipe tobacco had a pleasant aroma. We were content with listening to the crackle of the fire and watching the flames dance. The woods behind us were alive with singing crickets and tree frogs.

I said, "Hey Tobe! This must be the allure of camping!"

"Yeah man, see! We worked out the bugs we know how to do this shit now," Toby bragged.

I agreed, "Man we paid our dues and now we're outdoorsmen." It was turning into a pleasant evening.

My eyes adjusted to the encroaching darkness. The campfire was dwindling but it still gave us enough light to enjoy the evening and relax. Getting to sleep would not be a problem tonight.

The sky that night was unbelievable. Without light pollution or clouds the stars were ten times brighter than the night sky we were accustomed to seeing.

Toby pointed out various stars and constellations. The stars were time machines according to Toby. The light from the stars we see could have taken millions of years to reach us traveling at light speed. They showed us an image of what was when the light left that star.

I hadn't given that much thought before. We could never observe the universe in real time. Even light from our sun was eight minutes old when it reached us. Relaxing on our air mattresses in the dark we turned our full attention to the night sky. This night I noticed the dusty glow of the Milky Way! I'd never seen it so clearly before. It really was like a cloud spread across the sky.

"Toby, this is pretty goddamn cool. I bet this is how our ancestors entertained themselves for thousands of years."

"That's right," he agreed. I think he was proud of his plan.

"Toby just think, before there were televisions, people sat around a radio. Before that, the hearth was the evening gathering place for warmth and cooking. Before that, people sat by a campfire every night like we were doing at that moment."

"Yeah Terry it's kind of humbling," added Toby.

Over small talk, we polished off a final beer apiece. Our campfire had dwindled to the red radiance of embers. Darkness closed in like a fog, but it was okay! Our eyes had somewhat adjusted and the stars gave us enough light to see the meadow floor and the horizon. That's all we needed. "Serene" was the best word I could think of to describe the moment.

When our laughter faded everything fell still. It felt peaceful for a while. Then I noticed the forest was now silent. Not a single tree frog or cricket. Nothing. There were none of the other noises you expect to hear in the forest at night. Just an hour earlier the forest had been alive with noise. But now everything was so still it made me a little uneasy. It felt unnatural. I wanted Toby's opinion.

I said, "Toby, listen! ... Now that the fire's almost gone I can't hear the crickets anymore. I can't hear anything! Is that normal you think?"

He paused for a moment to listen. It was eerily silent. "They'll be back. Just wait an hour and they'll be back again." But Toby sounded a little less than confident.

We relaxed. Aside from a few missteps, we'd triumphed over a day spattered with disappointments. We did some cool exploring. We hiked probably six miles and enjoyed the beauty of the forest. No state campground would have given us the opportunities we had here! Any campground would have felt like a parking lot in comparison. Even the isolation was peaceful. Everything was calm. But the stillness of the forest had me unnerved.

I was still puzzled by our unscheduled nap in the woods. I chalked it up to a six-hour drive and the hike. There was no other explanation. I put it aside and just enjoyed the night sky.

I saw Toby turn his head away from me. Something odd caught his eye to the west. There were three identical points of light sitting low in the western sky. Toby asked, "Hey, check it out! Were those there a few minutes ago?"

"What? Those what?" I strained my eyes thinking maybe Toby's pulling my leg. "Toby don't bullshit me …"

"Right there," said Toby. "I don't think those are stars!" Toby pointed to three brilliant stars in a perfect little triangle sitting above the western horizon.

It took a moment of searching before I saw what he was talking about. Then I caught them. Each star was equidistant from the others. They sat stationary in the night sky. Whatever they were they were interesting. They looked like three very bright stars. All three were identical to one another and they twinkled in the night sky like very bright stars. For a while we just watched.

Toby broke the silence, "At least they're not like that freaky globe thing! That was weird."

"Yeah it was freaking weird Tobe!" We both feigned a laugh.

Toby said, "They look like bright stars to me. I don't know every goddamn star in the universe, but I know clusters and I notice when something looks peculiar. Terry these are … peculiar."

"I agree those are not stars Toby. There are no aircraft lights set-up in a configuration like that. So, what are they?" I asked.

Toby didn't answer my question. I had expected an explanation. We watched them for a quarter hour. They were now the focus of our attention. We both kept our eyes glued to these three points of light sitting stationary. They were now brighter than when we first began watching it.

Toby spoke up again. This time breaking twenty minutes of silence, "Man they're not aircraft and they're just sitting there. They're awfully damn bright too. There's no airfield around here, is there?"

"Nope," I told Toby. "Other than marijuana smugglers, who'd land a plane in a forest? This meadow is the only flat piece of land around for miles. It might be wide enough for a small airplane to set down."

"There!" Toby spotted it before me.

They were moving! It was exciting! We both spoke over one another. I said, "What the hell?" Neither of us had an answer. But it was cool. It was damn cool. I'd go as far as awesome.

While we watched, the three stars began to move. They slowly rotated as if on an axis. Unbelievable! All the while they maintained their perfect triangular configuration. The three lights moved in perfect harmony as if they were connected. For that reason, we suspected it might be a single solid object.

"Toby, if they are moving independent of one another someone has choreographed this beautifully," I said.

"You got that shit right!"

I asked, "Toby you're the astronomer. What the hell moves …?"

I left my sentence unfinished. I knew Toby had no idea either. There really was nothing to say. But we were spellbound.

"Hey man, are you as sleepy as I am?" asked Toby.

"Hell yeah, Tobe. We've been lying here watching this thing for an hour," I said with a yawn, "I'm beat … this day kicked my ass."

It began a vertical ascent. We watched it slowly climb the horizon. The points of light brighter as they crawled upward. These were not aircraft lights of any kind. This was something else entirely. I'm unsure how long we laid there just watching this thing. It was gaining altitude and incrementally increasing in brilliance and in size.

Toby didn't bother to use his cheap camera. His little camera was good for birthday parties but not long distant shots. We needed a camera and a telephoto lens like the one sitting on my kitchen counter.

We were content to just lay there and watch. Hardly a word was spoken between us. In the years following I will question our passive behavior that evening. It was too dark to see my watch, but I estimated it to be near 11:00 PM. The triangular formation grew larger and sped up a little.

Toby said, "Shit … they're really moving now."

I don't recollect responding. My eyes were stuck to them and I had nothing to add. It was moving even faster and blocking out entire fields of stars as it climbed. It was impossible to estimate its speed since we had no point of reference. Likewise, altitude was impossible to gage without knowing the object's size and location. Puzzled at how big or near this thing could be, I asked, "Toby, could we be seeing lights that are a million miles away or could they be cruising at aircraft altitude?"

"Terry man, that thing is in our atmosphere. It can't be outside of this solar system. No way. This thing is close. Man, I hope it's at cruising height … 35,000 feet would make me happy. No, I think it looks bigger because it's getting closer to us. It's … really close."

Toby said it first and confirmed what we both were thinking, "That's a single solid object. No doubt about it! Watch it pass over a field of stars. They blink out for a second or two and then blink back on as it goes past."

"I noticed that … Toby." With a feigned laugh I said, "I think that damn thing is headed toward us. I think it's going to sail right over the top of us."

Toby didn't say a word. Once more, I noticed how quiet the entire forest was. The crickets and tree frogs had not returned as Toby had predicted. It wasn't worth mentioning at the time. I felt uneasy but not frightened … yet. I asked, "Toby are we safe here?"

"Man, I sure hope so," Toby said. After a pause he added, "What could hurt us …?"

I wasn't quite sure if that was a question requiring a reply. I said nothing. We both watched as its path placed it directly over the meadow. Then it abruptly stopped.

"Toby it's not moving anymore is it?"

"Nope …"

It came to a halt at directly over our heads. While we watched the three points of the triangle spread further and further apart, eating up entire fields of stars as it grew. In a sky that was loaded with billions of stars it was like someone cut a giant triangle out of the sky. This was a single object and it was enormous.

The three stars on each point of the triangle were so bright that the entire meadow glowed as brilliantly as the full moon. It was bright enough to cast shadows.

All the anxiety had left me. Once it had parked over the meadow all emotion left me. We lay on air mattresses completely fascinated. We both just surrendered and let the calmness wash over us. It was pleasant, even soothing.

Grabbing our marginal flashlight Toby said, "I'm going to try and signal it and see what happens."

Before I could object Toby picked up the flashlight he held on his lap. Aiming it straight up he flashed the light three times.

I said, "Man, that might get someone's attention!" We waited to see what would happen. We didn't have to wait long for something to happen.

In an instant a beam of white light no wider than a softball was focused on our now dead campfire. It was about eight feet from where we lay. The light beam itself was visible. Like a high-powered search light shining through the fog. We never saw the beam descend. It was like someone threw a switch and there it was. It rested in the center of our fire pit.

Looking up we traced the source of the light beam. It came from below and center of the triangle. It stayed for no more than thirty seconds and was gone. Poof! It just shut off.

A few minutes passed. Then a blue light struck the campsite. It was tiny compared to white light but much more intense. It was only the diameter of a pencil or narrower. Lasers were still a new concept in 1977. I'd seen them on television. Just like the white light that preceded it, this blue light originated from the center of the triangle.

This intense blue light beam actively darted about the campsite. We never saw it move. Instead it would blink out and a millisecond later it was back on a different spot. Striking haphazardly, it darted all over our campsite never sitting on anything for more than a few seconds. It darted back and forth, and it had a hypnotic quality to it as we watched. I'm certain it landed on my leg and chest at least once. I saw it land on Toby once or twice too. Then it abruptly stopped. It was with us for no longer than one or two minutes.

With the blue light gone, we laid there silent and ambivalent. I had no emotion other than a pleasant feeling of sedation. This huge thing was still nearly over the meadow and we just watched it without comment. Then Toby said something like, "Show's over" or words to that effect. I don't think I replied.

Those were the last words spoken between us that evening. In unison we picked up our air mattresses and crawled into our tent. I felt the need to keep my boots on and laced up tightly. For that matter I didn't bother to undress at all.

The apathy felt all too familiar. These things, whatever they are and whoever they are, control our actions and our emotions. This was the same apathy I experienced in 1966. Thoughts about that 1966 experience flashed in my mind briefly.

I was asleep the moment my head hit the inflated plastic pillow. The heat was tolerable now, almost pleasant, but the forest was still dead silent. The only sound was Toby snoring softly.

Surviving

"Being abducted by alien beings

is akin to getting your arm caught in a piece of farming equipment,

you may get loose, but you'll surely lose something in the process."

Terry Lovelace

It was the lights that woke me up. I first noticed the bright lights and then that low bass hum I'd heard before, except this was more intense. Some flashes of light were bright enough to illuminate the tent's interior as if we'd had an overhead light.

My eyes were sensitive to the lights. When I maneuvered my body to get to my knees I realized I was in a lot of pain. Every bone in my body ached. I was insanely thirsty and scared too. I couldn't grasp what was happening to us and it was hard to shake off the sleep. I finally achieved a crouching position and my focus turned to Toby.

Toby was on his knees inside the tent. He had opened the tent flap about two inches and was peering out at something in the meadow. He was crouched down and captivated by whatever was happening there. Again, he muttered something, but I couldn't make out what he was saying.

The lights outside were multicolored greens and yellow. Very bright and in quick doses like a camera flash or a strobe light. I was awake but still in a fog.

I wondered if this could be park rangers with flashlights? Or maybe the headlights of a park service jeep with emergency lights flashing? But these were multicolored lights. That just didn't fit. I was struggling to fully wake up. I had to claw my way to consciousness.

It wasn't only the lights. There was also that droning sound. At first, I thought it was noise made by a generator. Who would be running a generator in the bed of a pickup truck? Game poachers maybe? The flashes of light illuminated the inside of the tent just enough to catch an image now and then. I saw Toby was trembling like a man in the cold. I realized I was trembling too.

I reached for the flashlight and Toby roughly snatched it from my hand. He held his finger across his lips and whispered, "Be quiet, they're still out there!"

I was shocked! In the flashes of light, I could see tracks down Toby's cheeks. He'd been crying! This is a man I knew well. We were first responders and we'd been through some dangerous moments together as a team. Toby could be relied upon to keep his head and not panic in an emergency. This felt like an emergency. What could move Toby to tears?

Toby continued to shush me when I tried to speak. With my voice just above a whisper I asked, "Toby what is it? Tell me what's wrong? Are there park rangers outside?"

Toby shook head "no" and stayed fixated on whatever was happening outside our tent. I noticed his breathing was shallow and quick, nearly panting.

I kept my voice at a whisper, "Toby, man, you got to slow your breathing down. You're hyperventilating. Toby you've got to tell me what's going on damn it?"

Then I froze. I was startled by motion outside the tent. There were shadows crossing between the tent and the source of the lights. I heard footsteps too. There was a rustling of leaves and grass. I had the impression maybe a dozen people were walking around the campsite. We both froze until the noises stopped.

The apathy we'd experienced before bed was long gone. In its place was abject terror and panic. I tried once more to get through to my friend.

"Toby, tell me what happened? Tell me who's out there?" I asked. But why even ask? I knew who was out here. I knew them.

Toby didn't answer me. I thought he was in shock. Frustrated I struggled to knees to see what was going on in the meadow. With my left arm I pushed Toby back a bit and gathered the courage to look for myself. I was fully awake now and the mental fog had mostly lifted.

Squeezing next to Toby, I pulled back the canvas and there it was. This wasn't a flying saucer at all! It was something else, something much bigger. This was something I had never seen before and was unprepared for. It was so gigantic that it filled every inch of the meadow. It sat motionless in mid-air. I estimated it to be thirty-feet off the meadow floor.

Then it registered. Of course, this is the thing we watched last night! Before we went to sleep in the tent we had been staring at something in the sky! I remembered we were watching the triangle in the sky, but it was about 2,500 feet above us last evening. This was the thing that generated so much disinterest in us just hours earlier? Unbelievable.

Now it was thirty feet over the meadow. We could see two sides clearly. There were randomly disbursed square panels of light on each side. It reminded me of a five story office building at night with offices lit here and there on every floor. Along the very top was a row of larger windows that slanted outward. They were all lit. I saw faint shadows and movement behind these larger panels. These larger panels stretched the entire length of the two sides of the triangle we could see.

The points of light had dimmed and were flashing. They were changing colors from greens, yellows, and orange. Along with the droning sound, these were the colored lights that woke me. The forest was quiet but for a low droning sound that reverberated in my chest.

Toby shoved his way over my left shoulder now and we watched together. We saw figures walking and milling around underneath this thing. My God they were children! Maybe a dozen or more kids, all about the same height. They were milling about in small groups of two or three.

I whispered to Toby, "What the hell are children doing here underneath this giant thing in the middle of the night?"

There was fear in Toby's voice when he answered, "Those ain't little kids. Those are not human beings Terry. They took you too … they hurt us both. Terry, they hurt us …" His voice faded into soft sobbing again. I placed my left arm across his shoulder and he leaned against me, crying like a child.

Images flashed in my mind and I recalled dreadful things. "Toby, I know." I shut them out.

I shifted my focus back to the craft as Toby struggled to compose himself. The thing was mind-blowing. I tried to take in the details. Its size alone made it a threat. It was made of black metallic material that was non-reflective. I would call the finish matte, like the diamond thing we saw. The corner nearest to us was the source of the multi colored lights we saw shining through the canvas of our tent. The lights on each point shined through a seamless panel that ran from the bottom to the very top. It was the three corner lights that we initially mistook for stars in the sky. They shined brilliant white lights that twinkled to give the casual observer the impression they were just three stars in a field of billions.

Turning my head, I glanced through the little screen window in the rear of the tent. Behind us the entire forest was dimly lit with long shadows. That sight unnerved me too. I knew I did not want to leave the tent.

A column of white light was now pouring out of something that was in the dead center of the craft's bottom. I estimated the diameter of this shaft of light to be thirty feet and perfectly round. It was a visible cylinder of light.

I was scared to death! But I didn't want to take my eyes off it. We saw the little people walk into the broad beam of light and dissolve into it. They continued moving under the light and disappearing two or three at a time. They were leaving. We watched until the last one was gone.

Shortly after the last little person vanished the center light switched off. The corner lights went to all white and were as bright as sunshine. The hum was gone now. The meadow was silent again.

We were on our bellies with just our heads sticking out of the tent. We watched. We both felt like something was about to happen. Something did.

The whole thing began to rise like a hot air balloon. It slowly rotated clockwise a half turn and wobbled slightly. It continued to climb, and it picked up speed until it was back in the heavens again. We watched the three points of light grow dimmer and closer together. Eventually it was just three dim dots of light forming a small triangle. This was the reverse of what we witnessed earlier in the evening. It didn't shoot out of sight or slide down to the horizon. It just continued its steady ascend until it vanished.

Toby spoke up, "It's gone now." He had regained control of his breathing and returned to his senses. I felt a little better too. But I ached all over and I was still terrified.

I had some memories of what had just happened to us inside the craft. I could see scant color images. I could recall a whirring noise and a sense of motion. Then a flash of bright light and we were suddenly inside the spacecraft. We were sucked into the thing just like the little people we watched dissolve into the light. I remember being awestruck by the volume of its interior. Everything was either in white or stainless steel. The structure was brilliantly lit inside. The ceiling and wall panels emitted light.

I was astounded to see three flying saucers parked inside. They were aligned in a neat row at the far side. We could see walkways and different levels. I recalled inside there were support structures and unrecognizable symbols etched into the walls.

We were not alone. Inside we saw fifty or sixty other people. Afterward I wondered who they were and what happened to them? Did they leave with the machine? Were they even still alive? I knew that I was fortunate to be alive.

There's a psychiatric disorder known as "survivor guilt." It happens when you survive a life-threatening event that others did not. Toby and I made it back, but I'm not sure those poor souls ever made it home. I sure as hell wouldn't change places with them.

I knew there had to be more. A lot more. But those few memories were the extent of my recall.

Many years later, events would happen to bring those memories back and into sharp focus. I recalled sights and voices I was supposed to forget. Like Betty and Barney Hill, it would need to be dredged-up from my subconscious. They could suppress the memories but never erase them.

The spacecraft was gone, and we sat upright afraid to speak above a whisper. Then I noticed my boots. My boots had been tightly laced before I laid down. I kept them that way intentionally. Now they were unlaced more than half-way down. That made no sense. I pulled them both off and discovered my socks were on crooked as well. I put them back on properly. Glancing to my left I noticed Toby was lacing-up his boots too.

I was aware of the pain again. Every fiber in my body ached. I felt sick and nauseous. But most of all, I was thirsty. I was insanely thirsty.

Toby rummaged around the tent and found the last warm can of beer. I had a gallon jug half-full of warm water. We split them both and craved more. Never in my life had I been so thirsty. It crossed my mind that I could take it all. I could gulp it down before he could stop me. I squelched that idea. I forced myself not to dwell on the thirst for fear I'd lose my mind.

"Toby, no matter what the hell just happened to us, we need to pull our shit together. I want to get to the car and get the hell off this goddamn meadow."

Toby nodded in agreement.

We needed a plan of action. Just like camping, this wasn't rocket science.

Toby had a plan, "I got this flashlight to read my map. I say we bolt out of this tent and into the car. You drive, and I'll tell you where to go. The maps still in the glove box. It's the same thing we did to find this place but in reverse. Man, we can do this."

Toby's confidence bolstered my own.

"Okay, you're right Tobe. Let's make a run for the car. You carry the flashlight and I've got my wallet and keys," I said with determination.

We readied ourselves. It sounds odd but leaving the tent and being in the open and exposed was a chilling thought. In the short distance we'd sprint to the car we'd be exposed and vulnerable. I hoped we'd feel safer once inside the car. The Impala offered locking doors and high-beam headlights. Most importantly it gave us mobility. I grabbed the rusty kitchen knife too. For what purpose I don't know. I just felt better with the knife in my hand.

Toby nodded with approval. I was sure he could use his map to guide us back. So long as his batteries held out. If we lost our flashlight our ability to navigate would be severely compromised.

I unzipped the tent all the way and we bolted for the car without a word said.

Toby was out first, and I followed. With nothing but starlight to see, we sprinted the 20 yards to the car. I stumbled at least once. Toby reached the car before me, but he was locked out. I locked the car purely out of habit.

I made it to the car a second or two behind Toby. I unlocked the driver's door and dove in. I slid across the plastic bench seat and unlocked Toby's door as I slammed my door shut behind me. With Toby inside, we both locked our respective sides of the car. It started right up. I kicked on the high beams and we were ready. The dome light stayed on for about sixty seconds. It was long enough to check the backseat and floorboard.

Before pulling out Toby asked urgently, "Are we good? Are you sure we're good?"

I understood him clearly, "We're good to go," I said reassuringly.

Toby's focus was dedicated to his map and the road ahead. The flashlight grew dimmer by the minute. Every now and then he'd reach over and turn on the dome light for a few seconds to better study his map. He needed the light to read the map but the light inside the car made me blind. I couldn't see the road. Not that there was anything outside that I wanted to see save the road in front of me. What caused two grown men to flee like scared little boys? Whatever happened on the meadow triggered a deep fear in the both of us. I was acquainted with the feelings. The disinterest and apathy were nothing new.

There was a reason my boots were unlaced. It was inadvertent validation by my captors. It was as much evidence as a curtain tucked into the venetian blinds. It was as good as a toy airplane on the floor. There's no way Toby and I just experienced the same dream or same hallucination. This was a real experience. Thirst was an immediate problem. But a solution would have to wait until we had some distance between us and that damn meadow.

This must be the kind of fear that men are born with. It comes from down deep in the lower part of our brainstem. This can't come from the cognitive part of the brain we use in decision-making. This came from a much older part of the brain. A leftover from our early evolutionary development. The same applied to our fear of the dark. Maybe that was a leftover from the long nights our distant ancestors endured? In the darkness of night, the tables were turned for them. Man became the prey. An unseen adversary had already gotten the drop on us while we were sleeping. Now was the time for flight because we were now the prey.

The car was made without seatbelts. It was all I could do to keep a grip on the steering wheel. Toby was violently tossed around inside the car like some crazed carnival ride. The high beams danced ahead of me as the car bounced along the road. Sometimes they lit-up the road. On hills they shown up in the trees and sometimes just two feet in front of us on the down side. Other than the two piercing headlights, we were enveloped by darkness.

I thought briefly about what we had left behind. We abandoned a perfectly good tent and air mattresses back there. The backpack with Toby's camera and our blankets were still inside the tent. We could care less. Our focus was drink, distance, and home—in that order.

We past the two posts where the road had been chained. Then I knew we were alright. I could find my way through the park and back to the road by myself. I complimented Toby for getting us back inside the park safely. But Toby lay sideways on the seat in a semi-fetal position. He was already snoring.

I shifted my focus to staying alert and staying on the road. The sunshine was so intense it was excruciating. My eyeballs ached.

It was mid-morning before Toby stirred. He broke the quiet hum of the road, "Man get us something to drink please." His voice was raspy like mine.

"Toby, I'm as thirsty as you are," I said. "I'll pull over at the next gas station we find. Hang on Tobe," I said, trying to sound reassuring.

"That sounds good. I'm just so damn thirsty."

I asked Toby, "Hey look around the car again. See if you can find us something else to drink. I'll drink anything wet that won't poison me."

Toby rummaged through the car for a jug or bottle. He searched for anything we could drink, "Sorry man, there's nothing left."

Still groggy from his sleep Toby was struck by the intensity of the sun and his thirst. Like me he was in pain from unbearable body aches. I felt flushed. I must have been feverish. Fever was the cause of the body aches and the thirst I reasoned. I itched all over too. It was that creepy feeling like I've heard people say they felt "bugs crawling under their skin." That's how it felt.

I couldn't recall a time ever in my life when I felt so parched. The sunlight was so intense. I wore a cheap pair of sunglasses, but they were worthless. My eyes stung as if I'd stared at the sun.

I said, "Toby, man this sunshine is killing me!"

Toby just nodded. His eyes were nearly swollen shut.

Soon we pulled into a "Gas 'n Go" touting, "the coldest beer in town." It was pretty much a clone of the place we hit on the way down. Just another generic stop for farmers and travelers. I'm sure it was indispensable for the locals. The second we stopped rolling I jumped out of the car and ran to the restroom. I shouted over my shoulder to Toby, "I'll be quick."

I noticed my legs were unsteady. Knocking on the beat-up steel door I yelled out with urgency, "Hello!" After a minute or two with no reply I made my way inside to find the key for the men's room.

An elderly gentleman manned the cash register. He appeared to be in his eighties but looked spry and sturdily built. He wore a tee shirt and well-worn overalls. He was waiting for me with a broad smile, a restroom key in hand.

I snatched it from his hand, "Thank you!" The restroom key was fastened by a length of chain to a foot-long piece of 4x4. Holy shit. They must have a serious problem with people driving away with their restroom key. I made it back to the men's room probably moments before I would have pissed myself.

Predictably, the place was filthy. There was no window and the only light came from a single buzzing neon tube. Stepping up to the urinal, I relieved myself for what felt like five full minutes. I thought to myself, "God no wonder I'm dehydrated." I went to the sink and was shocked when I saw my reflection in the mirror. It took a moment to register. My face was puffy and red, and my eyes were nearly swollen shut. Pulling my tee shirt over my head I saw dozens of angry red sores evenly dispersed and covering my entire face and torso. I dropped my pants to find that red spots covered both of my legs down to my boots. They itched savagely.

We had regularly doused ourselves down with military grade DEET. I expected to suffer a mosquito bite or two, but this was insane. I looked like a smallpox victim.

Then I saw how badly sunburned I was on my face and arms. My whole body was beet red. My upper arms, even under my arms were badly burned. Thankfully I wasn't blistered. I used DEET and sunscreen so what the hell? Did they cancel out one another when combined? I was searching for an answer but that was nonsense.

I had no tan lines whatsoever. To be burned so evenly I would have to had been fully nude in direct sunlight and rotated like a chicken on a rotisserie. How else could my body be so evenly burned?

Splashing tepid water all over my head and chest, I rinsed myself off as best I could. The water felt good. It felt like ice water when I splashed it on my chest. I didn't bother to dry off. I soaked my tee shirt so the wind from the highway could help cool me down on the last leg of our trip. I still felt feverish. The thirst was still with me. Cupping my dirty hands under the grungy faucet to drink, I noted my hands were shaking. I drank and drank from what trickled out of the dirty faucet. Repeating the process. I drank until I felt I could hold no more.

I opened the metal door. Standing there was a pathetic looking Toby, patiently waiting. He looked like he could fall over any instant. He was unsteady. He leaned against the cinderblock wall to keep from toppling over.

Crap, if I looked bad, Toby was a train wreck by comparison. In addition to the insect bites, Toby's eyes were red like mine. His entire face was swollen sufficiently to distort his features. He complained of the burn on his black skin. He was in agony.

I handed Toby the restroom key. I said, "No worries pal. I'll finish the drive and you can go back to sleep."

"Thanks Terry," Toby said as he pushed his way past me and into the men's room.

The second I stepped outside, I was momentarily blinded by the sun. I pulled my sunglasses down and headed back inside to buy something cold to drink.

A bell over the door tinkled when I walked back inside the little store. The old man hadn't moved. I paid for our gas and bought a six-pack of orange soda.

"My buddy will be right back with the key," I said.

"That's okay son. Nobody makes it too far away with the key," he said. I think the key-thing must have been an inside joke. I sat my orange six-pack on the counter and held out a ten. He must have noticed my hands were shaking. He put on his glasses and eyed me up and down while he made change.

He was straight out of a farm equipment calendar. He wore the green tractor hat and well-worn overalls. A pouch of chewing tobacco sat next to the register. Alongside was an old diner-style coffee mug he used as a spittoon. The old guy looked me over a second time. Then he asked me with genuine concern, "It ain't none of my business but what the hell have you fellers been into?"

I answered honestly, "I don't know." I shrugged my shoulders and returned his smile.

"You better get to someplace where you can get yourself some help," he said, before stuffing a golf ball size chunk of chewing tobacco in his cheek. "You boys want to call somebody for a ride or something? You can use my phone if you want. Hell, I don't care," he said. He was the first bright spot in an otherwise miserable day.

"We're just headed to the air base. I think we'll be okay," I was touched by his concern for our safety. I thought, some people are born with empathy for others and some are born with none. I don't remember thanking him but I'm sure I did.

I heard the bell tinkle again as Toby stumbled inside to buy something to drink. He chose a gallon of grape drink for himself. I thought, he sure as hell isn't drinking any of this! Then I felt ashamed for my selfishness. I grabbed my orange soda and stumbled to the car. The sun was merciless. It hit me like a punch in the face.

I jumped into the driver's seat and re-adjusted my mirror. Simultaneously, Toby climbed into the passenger seat. He cuddled up with a gallon jug of grape-aid against his chest. I'm sure the cold jug felt good against his burned torso. Toby immediately began pounding the grape drink while I polished-off six cans of orange soda, one after another. I craved more.

"Go back to sleep, Tobe. I got it the rest of the way." I knew there was no way he could drive a car.

We never once discussed the events of the past 12 hours. For that matter, we rarely spoke at all during the ride back. Something had changed. Things were different between us. We were different.

Toby mumbled, "God I can't wait to get back ..." and his voice trailed off.

Neither of us were in any mood for chit chat. He went back to his grape drink. In fifteen minutes he had downed the last of it and returned to his fetal position. A few minutes later he was out like a light and snoring again. I envied him. I couldn't wait for my turn to shut my eyes.

Back on the road a pounding headache behind my eyes made driving tougher than before. It was from the sunlight. The fever and body aches hadn't eased.

Soon, I fell back into the rhythm of the road and traveled on autopilot. The warm air from the highway completely dried my shirt before I made fifty miles. I was dangerously tired from lack of sleep and had no business driving. Toby was in worse shape than me. I couldn't give him the keys.

Have you ever been so tired that you begin dreaming while awake? Once I caught myself nod off for what seemed like a split second! I raised my head and when I opened my eyes I was in the lane of opposing traffic on my left. By the grace of God, the road was empty that morning. Had things been different I could have killed us and probably another innocent soul or two. From that point on I concentrated on the road and staying awake. I had a newfound respect for long-haul truckers.

I reviewed the events of the previous night over and over. What happened to us once we were inside that giant airplane hangar? Something very bad had happened. Someone had hurt the both of us. Bits and pieces of terrible things floated by my mind's eye. I winced at the images and once or twice involuntarily yelled-out, "No!" hoping to drive the scenes from my mind. I did my best to focus on something else.

My memories were like flipping through a stack of photographs under a strobe light. There were horrible images. There were garbled auditory sounds and voices with unintelligible words mixed together. I very clearly remembered Toby kept screaming!

Visually, it was limited to a series of disjointed images. I had no memory whatsoever of what may have occurred during our four-hour unscheduled nap on that outcropping of limestone. But I believe something happened.

From the time I entered the tent until that moment, I simply couldn't place events on a linear timeline. But in a flash of intuition, I surprisingly knew what had happened to us! We'd been set up! We were there by design. We had an appointment on the meadow that evening, and we arrived right on time. Looking back at this ridiculous camping trip idea and the way we went about it was almost comical. In a tragic way.

I couldn't speak the words out loud, but I knew they took me. I knew they took both of us. This wasn't anything like seeing a flying saucer. I'd seen flying saucers before and it was a cool experience! It was exciting. I knew it was real because I validated that second event with a piece of curtain stuck into the venetian blinds. That happened when I was eleven-years old. There was nothing cool about this experience and I had more than enough evidence to validate it. It would turn out that I had more evidence than I ever could have suspected.

I wondered if they took Toby when he was little. Maybe that's why he has such a fascination with space? It's a pity I would never have an opportunity to ask him. I glanced over to the softly snoring Toby. I could sense something was different between us and I didn't understand it. During the entire trip home there was only essential conversation. In retrospect, I'm not even sure Toby was asleep! He may have just faked it to avoid conversation. That was fine with me. I wasn't in my right mind.

It was a state of mind that I'd come to know even better in the days and years to come. It was sad that we returned so empty handed. There would be no laughing or making jokes over a beer at his barbeque. I wouldn't be teasing Toby about the starry-eyed farm girl. Forget everything. It was just not a topic for discussion. Ever.

We had promised to call our wives. This was the time before cell phones. But they didn't expect to hear from us for another day, so it was no big deal. I just sped toward home miserable and fighting to keep my eyes open and my car in the correct traffic lane.

If I had called home from the gas station using the old man's phone what would I say? The old guy sat two feet away from the phone. That would have been a call he'd remember. I could just imagine the look on his face when he overheard that conversation. "Hi Hon! Yeah, we're headed back early. Why? Oh, well we saw a giant triangle that blotted out the stars and went to bed. Then there were crazy lights and we were dragged aboard a giant space ship. So, we're coming home early, and goddamn am I thirsty!"

I could just imagine the old guy swallowing his chaw of tobacco.

My mother's words came back to me, "Terry thinks he saw a spaceship and he's throwing a fit." I wanted to throw a fit. After an insanely miserable ride we were finally close to home. It was time to wake up Toby. He'd been soundly asleep since downing his last drop of his grape-aid.

I announced, "Hey pal our ETA is about fifteen minutes."

Toby mumbled something and stretched. I took it to mean, "okay" or some similar word of acknowledgement. He was having trouble adjusting his eyes to the sunlight. I was certain Toby was hurting more than I was.

Finally, we were back on base. First stop was Toby's house. I unceremoniously dropped him off in his driveway. Other than his flashlight he had no baggage to carry in. His backpack was back at the campsite. Our parting words were, "See ya."

We lived just a few blocks from Toby's. My wife heard me pull into the driveway. She was happy to see me but puzzled why the trip had been cut short?

"Glad to have you back, but why'd you come home so soon, you know you forgot your…?" She noticed something wasn't right.

I moved past her and sat at our kitchen table. I recall asking, "What do we have to drink? I am so thirsty."

She looked at me for a long moment before she spoke. All she could say was, "What the hell?" She poured me a tumbler full of lemonade. I drank it all in two gulps. She poured more.

"How did this happen to you, Terry? Is Toby in the same shape?" she asked.

I shrugged my shoulders and mumbled, "I think Toby's worse."

She found the thermometer and took my temperature. Five minutes later she said, "Jesus, you've got a temp of 104!" She gave me some aspirin and drew me a cool bath.

In ten minutes she had me undressed and soaking in cool water. She added baking soda or something that helped with the itching and the sunburn pain. It felt so good to just soak and relax in the water. I laid there for about 30 minutes guzzling instant lemonade on ice. She took my temperature again and it had dropped to just over 102.

"Come on! I'll help you get dressed we're going to the clinic," she said.

Before I knew it, I was in the exam room.

One of the doctors walked in with a look of concern. For some reason I expected him to ask, "what the hell you two fellers been into?" Like the old guy at the gas station who was so kind.

"Hey Terry, what the hell happened to you guys? You're both pretty sick. Brenda will draw some blood and push it through the lab stat. Your wife tells me you were out with Tobias on a camping trip and came home this morning sick as dogs. Is that correct so far?"

I nodded.

He immediately began examining me while my favorite nurse, Brenda, drew a dozen tubes of blood. "You guys felt fine the evening before. Then you woke up sick sunburned and bug bitten and running a temp of 104? Is that right?"

"Yes, that's right."

He wanted the entire story, "Okay tell me what happened to you guys?"

I told him most of the story leaving, out all that happened between 9:00 PM the preceding evening and 3:00 AM early this morning. Most of it was a blur anyway.

I knew I'd end up on the psych-ward if I told him the true story. So, I gave him my sanitized version and focused on my physical symptoms and not my recollections.

As I spoke, more and more people trickled into the room. I could hear my wife's voice in the hallway. I heard someone say, "Tobias." So, I knew Toby must be here too.

There were now three doctors, and a second nurse joined Brenda. Doctors came and went. I guess they were trying to treat both of us at the same time. I'm sure they were as perplexed as we were. It seemed that way. I didn't know it at the time, but we were classified as acutely ill.

I endured the most thorough medical examination of my life. It was difficult to know what was going on. My eyes ached and were sensitive to the light, so I kept them closed for most of the exam.

A medical assistant brought in a camera and photographed every single inch of my body. Brenda counted every red spot. The grand total was 124. At one point I heard the growl of a Geiger counter and got a glimpse of the signature yellow box.

I knew about radiation. I was on an air base with enough plutonium to destroy all of Western Europe. I heard the Geiger counter growl. That concerned me. Exposure to radiation in the woods was an unsettling thought. Exposure to radiation inside a spaceship was too much to fathom.

One of the doctors asked Sheila to go home and bag up everything I brought back from the trip. He asked her to go right now and bring it all right back.

He gave her a large white bag with the Bio Hazard symbol on it and a drawstring at the top. He wanted everything I was wearing when I came home, boots, socks, dirty clothes the whole lot. He also wanted anything I brought home with me, like rocks or anything of the like.

I sure as hell didn't bring home any souvenirs.

My commanding officer came in. It was common knowledge throughout the unit that Toby and I were going on this camping trip. I wasn't sure how he'd react. He came to check on my condition. Like everyone else he wanted to know how we both managed to get so sick.

I said, "Sir, I have no idea. But I'll be up and about for my Tuesday night shift."

"We can cover it if we have to, just get well, alright Ansel Adams? We want to see your photographs as soon as you get a few prints developed. Just get some rest."

I didn't know it at the time, but he reported the details of our hospitalization to the security police. I assume it was protocol because of the bizarre nature of our injuries and positive reading on the Geiger counter.

I told our CO thanks. Then I thought, Oh, shit! I won't have a single photograph to show him or anyone else. That seemed like the last indignity of the day. I fought to keep from crying.

The examination finally wrapped up. As the doctors left, Brenda helped me off the table and into a wheelchair. She also got me more ice water, which was very much appreciated.

"Doctor Sanders admitted you with a diagnosis of dehydration. That IV is running full-tilt so you should feel better soon."

I was relieved to hear I wasn't suffering from radiation poisoning.

Brenda assured me, "When Sheila comes back, we'll make sure she knows where to find you."

"Thank you so much. Brenda, you're so kind."

Special Agents

My first forty-eight hours in the hospital are a blur. I don't know what they gave me for pain, but I slept almost around the clock. They kept the lights off in my room unless needed, because I was still photophobic.

It was the evening of my last night in the hospital. I'd describe my condition as marginally okay. Hopefully well enough to go home in the morning. The CO gave me a week off duty to regain my strength. I needed every minute of it.

A nurse opened my door and two men in business suits followed her in. She ignored them and walked over to my bed and said, "Dr. Sanders ordered something to help you rest tonight. You'll be going home in the morning." She held a syringe and said she was going to give me something for pain. I could use it. Every bone in my body still hurt. At least the itching had abated.

The older of the two gentlemen intercepted her. He said, "If that's going to sedate him it'll have to wait. We're from OSI and need to ask Sergeant Lovelace a few questions. This won't take long; shut the door on your way out." She was out like a shot and I didn't get my pain medicine. The instant the door was closed the older guy flipped on the overhead lights. It felt like I had sand in my eyes.

The OSI is the investigative arm of the USAF's Security Police. They are to the air force what NCIS is to the navy. They carried themselves like Gestapo.

"Sir, can you turn off the lights? Please. They hurt my eyes."

"We need to see what we're doing, son. We can't talk to you in the dark. This won't take long, I just have a couple questions," he said.

They introduced themselves as special agents from the OSI. They were all business and scared the hell out of me with their affect and demeanor. They showed me their badges. Since they wore civilian clothes, I inspected their credentials just long enough to catch their rank. The older guy was a major and his companion was a captain.

Each man grabbed a chair and they sat on opposite sides of the bed close to my head. The older guy commandeered control of my tray table and moved everything off the top. He slid it over my lap while his partner raised the head of my bed to a sitting position.

I'm fuzzy about the captain's name but I can clearly remember the older guy. He introduced himself as, "Special Agent Gregory." Agent Gregory was in charge and did most of the talking.

The captain introduced himself as, "Special Agent something." He set up a small reel-to-reel tape recorder on my tray table. He crossed his legs and balanced a notepad on his knee. He said very little but paid keen attention.

Special Agent Gregory spoke first, "Sergeant Lovelace, I'll be the special agent in charge of your case."

"Yes sir," I said. But I thought to myself oh shit! I have a case? What the hell does that mean? Did we burn down the forest? I knew the reputation of the OSI for being tough guys.

I dared ask, "Agent Gregory sir, am I in trouble?"

He replied, "Son, you're asking me if you're in trouble? Would we be here if you weren't in trouble?" His reply amused the captain. My stomach turned. I caught the sarcasm in his tone. I sized him up as someone not to mess with. He wore a flattop haircut and had the chiseled square jaw look. His pistol was visible inside his unbuttoned suit coat.

Special Agent Gregory explained, "Sergeant Lovelace, we need to talk to you right now while everything is fresh in your mind. Do you understand? I know you're sleepy, but you need to stay alert. It's important that you answer my questions honestly and thoroughly. Do you understand me Sergeant?"

I nodded.

Agent Gregory rolled his eyes. I saw he was annoyed, but I didn't know why. He took a laminated playing card from his breast pocket and put on some reading glasses. They rested on the very tip of his nose, so he could see over the top.

He read my rights under the Uniform Code of Military Justice also known as the UCMJ. He recited them like he'd read them a thousand times. The tone and tenor of his voice betrayed his distaste for the task. He took off his glasses and carefully put them away when he'd finished.

Without eye contact he asked, "Do you understand what I've told you?"

Once more I nodded and once more he looked annoyed. Now he raised his voice, "Son, don't answer me with a nod of your head or a shrug of your shoulders. The Captain here can't put that down in his notes and the tape recorder can't pick it up. Do you get it now? Now speak up!"

"Yes sir, now I understand," I said apologetically.

Reaching into his briefcase, Agent Gregory pulled out a manila folder and a few papers. On my tray table he carefully laid out six forms. He instructed me, "Son, these are waiver and consent forms. You're waiving your rights and giving us your consent for certain things. You're promising to cooperate fully and honestly with our investigation. You have the right to an attorney if you'd like. You can hire your own lawyer, or the JAG will appoint someone to represent you. You said you understood your rights. Do you understand them, or shall I read them to you again?"

"Yes, sir and no sir." I said. I believe he was intentionally mixing his questions, so they required mixed "yes" and "no" responses. It made the process difficult to follow. Probably an interrogation technique taught at the Gestapo academy.

Agent Gregory picked-up where he left off, "By signing these consent forms you give us permission to conduct a search of your home and your car. We have your permission to seize anything we find without first securing a search warrant. We look for things such as contraband or anything that could be evidence of a crime. You don't have anything to hide from us, do you ... son?"

"No sir," I said. I felt like voicing an objection would make me sound evasive or uncooperative. I was afraid of this guy.

"Let's be clear. You understand what I've said, and you are fine with all of it?"

I spoke up this time, "Yes sir."

"Good," said Gregory, obviously pleased with himself. He used his finger to show me where to sign, "I need your signature here and here, sign here and here and here, here and the last one. I also need your initials here on the left. Very good…very good. Well done Sergeant."

I signed everything. I never read a single word of it. My eyes were still nearly swollen shut. Reading them would have been impossible. His explanations were woefully inadequate for a young and naïve NCO.

Gregory swooped-up the forms and returned them to his manila folder. Projecting his voice in the direction of the tape recorder Agent Gregory said, "This is Special Agent Gregory, in the matter of Sergeant Terry J. Lovelace, 351st Strategic Missile Wing …"

While he spoke, I closed my eyes because of the pain. I guess he thought I was falling asleep. Gregory startled me by shouting, "Pay attention! Stay with me and don't forget to speak up when you answer my questions. Got it son?!"

"Yes sir," I understood him alright.

I dared to ask a question, "Sir, is there a way we could do this after I've had some more sleep?"

They paused for a moment and looked at each other. I think they were amused!

Scowling at me, Agent Gregory said, "Look sergeant, I've already explained why we need to talk now. Are you rescinding your agreement to cooperate now?"

I said, "No sir, I just ..."

"You just what son? I read your rights and explained them. You claimed to understand them. You signed consent forms and waivers. Nobody twisted your arm or threatened you. Do you want me to tear these papers up now? If you'd like we can stop right this minute and we'll see each other again at your court martial," replied Gregory.

"No sir, I mean yes sir, I'll cooperate... sir." The words "court martial" evoked all kinds scenarios. None of them were good.

"Excellent! While all of this is fresh in your memory we want to get to the truth. The doctors want us to help them find an explanation for what's happened to you and your friend," he said.

"Yes sir. I was just asking. I want to cooperate. I'll answer your questions sir," I didn't want him to think I was hiding something.

"Alright. So, Sergeant Lovelace you agree to answer my questions now fully and honestly?"

"Yes sir," I said, raising my voice to satisfy him.

"You and Senior Airman Tobias went on a camping trip to Devils Den Park and Nature Preserve in northern Arkansas. That wildlife preserve is federal land. Did you know that?" he said in an ominous voice, emphasizing "federal land."

"No sir," But I thought so what? What's the big deal?

Gregory asked, "Did you and Tobias stay at the park last night?"

"No sir," I said in the belief he was referring to the campgrounds and not the park in general.

Gregory went ballistic, "Bullshit! Then where'd you stay ... the Hilton? You didn't buy a camping permit and you didn't stay at the campgrounds! The park rangers found your abandoned campsite deep inside that nature preserve. If you're going to lie to me, I'll hang your ass, son!" His face was red and the veins in his neck stood out. Many years later in retrospect, I think his rage was all theatre. He set me up by asking multiple questions requiring yes and no responses. It was one of his ways to assert dominance and establish who was in charge.

I said as earnestly as possible, "Yes sir! I misunderstood. I thought by *park* you were referring to the campgrounds. No sir, honestly! I misunderstood you. We didn't buy a permit and we didn't stay in the campgrounds either. But yes ... we went into the wildlife area. All of the maps and directions showing where we went are still in the glove box of my car."

With a nod from Gregory the captain stood up and left the room.

Agent Gregory knew I was sufficiently intimidated. He said, "Son, I'll let that slide one time because you just might be that damn stupid. The park rangers found your campsite. You left behind a blanket that was marked *Property of the USAF* alongside your government issue DEET and sunscreen. Your buddy left his little camera and a backpack with his name and address on it. It wasn't too hard to track you two down."

"I understand sir," I said. I was sure there had to be more to this story. I knew it had to do with what we witnessed and experienced in that damn meadow. This was about the thing we saw. I'll be damned if I'd tell him what we saw. I remembered what happened when I told people about seeing a flying saucer.

Gregory asked me with honest curiosity, "Son, there are a dozen state parks within an hour's drive or less from here. Why would you drive half a day to go camping for two nights?"

I explained, "Sir, Toby suggested Devils Den. The location was his idea. I have a camera with a telephoto lens and a tripod. I hoped to get pictures of wildlife and some scenic shots. Toby is an amateur astronomer and he wanted to watch the stars. Devils Den has some high ground. We found a summit in the preserve that gave Toby a good view of the night sky and it gave me panoramic scenery in all directions."

"So, you and your buddy trespassed into the nature preserve and set up a camp. According to Tobias, you guys saw some stars that looked funny. Then you just went inside the tent and fell asleep around midnight. Is that right?" he asked.

"Yes sir," It sounded suspicious the way he phrased it.

He continued, "Then you got up and left at three o'clock in the morning. You got in your car and just left? Is that correct?"

"Yes sir, I know that sounds odd."

"Did you plan on coming back the next day? That's the only reason to leave everything behind. Do you have a little marijuana plot out there or something?"

I was shocked. My mind was racing. What if someone had a little weed garden out there? That could mean very big trouble if they tried to pin it on us. "No sir, we didn't plan to come back for anything and we sure didn't have any marijuana."

Gregory asked, "That's just odd. Don't you think? You two leave all your gear and abandon your campsite. Then after just three hours of sleep you drive halfway across the State of Missouri?"

"Yes sir, I guess it does sound crazy … sir."

Gregory shifted gears, "Crazy? You and your buddy saw some lights in the sky? Airman Tobias said you saw three lights that looked like stars. What did you see out there, son?"

"Sir, I saw the same thing. Three lights that looked like stars," I said.

Gregory asked, "How long did the two of you lay there and just watch these stars?"

"About three hours sir."

Looking shocked he yelled, "Three hours! Now think real hard and tell me exactly how many photographs of these stars you took during those three hours?"

I replied truthfully, "None sir. We just watched them and then went to bed."

Gregory looked puzzled. He said, "You what? You see something unusual and you didn't take a photograph? Everybody in your squadron says you're a photography nut and you didn't take a picture of something you thought was odd. Something Tobias said was almost over your heads?"

Now I was certain these guys had interrogated Toby. I had no way of knowing what he told Gregory and his sidekick. I tried to explain, "Sir, we just watched them for a couple hours and then we went to bed inside the tent. The stars were still up there when we turned in. We went to sleep around midnight."

Gregory scribbled some notes. After a long pause he asked, "Son, what were you planning to do on this trip exactly? You two want to look at the stars and take tourists pictures during the day? You could have stayed at the campground with hot showers and still have done all those things."

"Sir, I was hoping for some nature shots like wooded scenery and eagles."

Gregory asked, "And just how many shots of eagles and scenery did you take?"

"None sir." It was obvious he didn't believe me! I could read it in his face.

"Let's try again son! Tell me what you and Airman Tobias planned to do inside this nature preserve?"

"Sir, yes. We planned on hiking and doing some wildlife photography. I've got a 35mm camera with a good telephoto lens," I said. I felt uneasy now. I knew where this was headed, and I wasn't looking forward to telling him.

Sarcastically, Gregory asked, "So what do you photograph with this telescopic lens of yours when you're not trespassing onto federal land or bumbling around in a nature preserve?" I wasn't even sure it was a question.

"Sir, it's a telephoto lens not a telescopic lens," I said. I immediately realized it was a mistake to correct him.

He was furious, "Tele-what-the-fuck! For some reason you're just not going to tell me what you photographed... I need your camera and all the film."

"Sir, I can have my wife bring it ..." He interrupted me and shook his head.

"Unless you have film and a camera hidden somewhere forget it! We're conducting a raid on your home and car right now. So just tell me. Where's the camera and the film you took on the trip. All I need is that roll of film!"

"I left it at home, sir. It's sitting on my kitchen counter... unless my wife moved it. I didn't take a single picture because I forgot the goddamn camera." They're searching my home and my car? Did I hear him correctly? I asked, "Sir, you're searching my house and my car, right now?"

"Don't look so surprised Sergeant Lovelace. You just signed a consent form. You gave us your permission. I want your film and the camera you took on the trip. We'll develop your film for you. I just want to see what you've been photographing with this telescopic lens of yours."

"Sir I …"

I lost my train of thought as the captain came back into the room. He pulled up his chair and popped open his briefcase. Security policemen had already searched my home. They took my camera, film and all my prints. They took our car and scared the holy hell out of my poor wife.

From his briefcase, the captain retrieved Toby's hand drawn map and the tourist map we snagged at a kiosk. He handed them to Gregory, who put on his reading glasses and carefully inspected both for a moment.

Gregory placed them on the tray table in front of me and said, "Sergeant Lovelace, you're going to help me make sense of this. Explain these to me!"

"Sir, that's the map Toby drew so we wouldn't get lost trying to find our way out of the nature preserve when it was time to go home. This is the tourist's map we picked up near the visitor's center. The hand-drawn map shows our route inside the nature preserve. It picks up where the park's map ends," I said.

"Show me," Gregory demanded.

I placed the two maps side by side and used his pen to point, "Sir, here's where we left the park. Then we crossed here and drove into the wildlife area. We looked for a good open place to set up camp. Here is the high plateau where we stayed. It's a big open field. I call it a meadow."

He handed me a blank sheet of paper from his legal pad, "Draw the shape of the meadow for me as if you were looking down on it from above. Then draw a line to show where you drove into the meadow. Got it?"

"Yes sir." I said. It took just a second.

"Now draw a large arrow to point north and draw a little box where you parked the car. Try to keep it to scale as much as you can."

"Here sir, this area is all grass. Right here is where we parked my car and the arrow points north."

Gregory was pleased. His instructions continued, "Now draw a little circle where you set up your tent and show me where the tree line starts."

"Yes sir."

"Now, estimate the meadow's length and width for me?"

"Sir I'm not good at estimating distance," I confessed.

"Just use the length of your car. Use the car like the scale on a map. Just give me your best estimate," he said.

It took a couple minutes. "This is it, sir." I handed back his pen and my drawing.

Gregory studied it and stuck it in his folder with the maps and papers I signed. Then he turned his attention to the captain again, "You get his camera and film?"

"Yeah, we got a 35mm camera. It had a fresh roll of film in it but no exposures. We seized three unopened boxes of film. All black and white and all are high resolution. One is infrared made specially for use in poorly lit conditions or at night. They were all bought at the base exchange. The receipt is in the bag. There was nothing there under his name for pick up, I checked."

Gregory turned back to me now, "Son what kind of wildlife or scenic photography uses high resolution black and white film? What kind of scenery were you planning to photograph in the dark? You're going to have to explain that one to me too."

I did my best to explain, "Sir, I read a book from the library about Ansel Adams. He was a famous photographer 75-years ago. He's famous for his black and white prints of desert scenes and mountains. Black and white film makes high quality outdoor prints. I use it mostly to photograph eagles and the moon."

The captain rejoined the conversation, "We have every negative that was in the house. We got the wife's camera it's a cheap 35mm. It was in a bedroom drawer with seven exposures. We're processing that roll now. It should be ready in an hour."

"Very good." Gregory smiled.

The captain continued, "Sergeant Lovelace has a darkroom set-up. It's in the rear bedroom. We took all the negatives and prints. He seems fascinated with the full moon for some reason. We've got a dozen prints or so here. I thought you'd find them interesting. But not a single roll of exposed film."

Gregory's response was harsh and immediate, "Sergeant, where's the film from your trip?"

"Sir, I left my camera at home! When we were in the meadow, I didn't have a camera."

"I don't believe you son and that puts you in deep shit. Do you get it? I think you have a roll of film stashed somewhere. I don't understand why you need a darkroom either. Why don't you develop your film at the base exchange like everyone else?" Gregory asked.

"Sir, it's a cheap hobby if you develop your own prints. Plus, you can crop and enlarge images in the dark room and do all kinds of things."

Gregory wasn't dumb he knew that already. He had more knowledge about photography than he let show. Before Gregory could ask his next question, the nurse returned. She had a syringe in her hand and a look of determination on her face.

"Dr. Sanders wants Sergeant Lovelace to have his medication. I can bring the doctor down here if you like," she said with authority. OSI agents may be tough guys. But they're no match for a registered nurse.

"No need. I think we're about done here. I don't think Sergeant Lovelace has much more to add." He was annoyed by the interruption. The nurse gave me an injection and left.

Gregory turned his attention back to me. He didn't appear angry. He spoke calmly and asked, "Sergeant, where is the film? I need the negatives for every single photograph you took since you crossed the Arkansas border."

"Sir, I don't have any," I said.

Without telegraphing their move, both men abruptly stood and killed the tape recorder. They packed-up their things and moved toward the door. I was relieved.

Before he left the room, Gregory told me, "You're being reassigned but you'll be staying at Whiteman. You'll be reassigned and work in a support section. Those orders will be cut today but of course, that's all subject to change."

"Yes sir." I thought thank God. I get to finish my enlistment here, unlike Toby, and I'm not handcuffed to the bed.

Gregory continued, "You are ordered not to leave the base without permission from your CO or myself. You will not speak with Senior Airman Tobias or his family. You will not communicate with them in any way. That means no notes or letters. You will not discuss this incident with anyone at your new duty station or disclose the reason for your reassignment, are you with me, son?"

"Yes sir. I understand."

He added, "Don't attempt to contact Tobias through a third party either. That means your wife or anyone else. You will not talk about the lights you saw in the sky that night. Not to anyone. That means not your wife, not your priest, or your mother, no one. Do you understand me?"

"Yes, sir I understand everything," I said.

Then he paused. His demeanor changed and for a minute he just stared at me. Then he lowered his voice to a whisper, "You two knuckleheads stumbled onto something that made you very sick and I think you know what it was. Oh, I think you know what I'm talking about! Don't you son? I know you do."

"Yes ... sir," was all I could add.

"If you come across that other camera or if you have something you want to tell me just pick up the phone." He dropped a business card on my tray table. "There's my number, call me."

Then he smiled and even killed the overhead lights as he left! "Strange guy," I muttered as the door shut behind him.

A short while later my wife arrived. Tearful and overwhelmed by the raid on our home and our car being seized. I held her. I should say we held one another.

She had news too. "Tammy called me. They're being reassigned! They don't even know when or where. She told me not to call her or come over. She said it was an order."

Unbelievable! They sure as hell don't want us to compare our stories! To reassign Toby was just insane. To reassign me to a support unit was insane too, but far less harsh.

I couldn't reconcile my feelings. I didn't want anything to do with Toby or Tammy, ever. My feelings about Toby had changed. You'd think two people with a shared experience like this would be together and supportive of one another. It was the kind of event that bonds people. It wasn't supposed to distance us. But it did.

I gave her our good news, "I'm being reassigned to a support unit. That's a disappointment but I can finish out my enlistment here. I think the idea is to keep Toby and I separated until he ships out. Once he's gone I'm hoping to go back to work in the ER."

She was relieved too. But she shared my anxiety.

"Terry, I know you probably want to say goodbye to Toby. But they warned us. We're not supposed to have any contact with them. I'm afraid of these OSI people. Please cooperate and don't piss them off."

"Sheila, I promise I'll cooperate with them. Don't worry this will blow over. I promise."

My feelings about Toby had changed radically. I felt it in the car on our way home. I couldn't understand it. I felt relieved that Toby was leaving. He's a bad memory gone. I didn't want to see Toby again ever, except for a quick goodbye and "nice knowing you."

I would see Toby one last time despite my feelings. I'd violate Gregory's order of no contact. I'd risk going to jail to say goodbye to a man I wanted nothing to do with? It made no sense.

As I was being discharged from the hospital, one of the doctors stopped by. It was the older doctor who wanted me to have the chest x-ray. He sat on my bed and told me what to expect after I'm released from the hospital and "clear-up some loose ends."

"Sergeant you're being reassigned to a support unit. They really don't have a spot for you yet, but they'll keep you busy I'm sure."

That was disappointing news, but Agent Gregory told me it was coming.

"Sir, why can't I just go back to work in the ER?"

"The higher-ups asked us to find you something else to do until Tobias is off base. You're not going to reenlist. You're just running the clock until your enlistment's up. Do you want to stay in the ER and work the nightshift again with a new partner?"

"Yes sir, I'm a good EMT and I love my job. I'm an asset to the squadron."

"Maybe when things settle down you can get back to us. Your CO was sorry to learn you're being reassigned. We'll see if we can get you back on an ambulance before your enlistment's finished. But meanwhile, I have a few things I want you to know."

"Yes Sir."

"Keep your nose clean and your mouth shut, and everything will be okay. Just stay out of trouble and you have nothing to worry about. Tobias told us you guys were drinking out there. The burns that you two suffered were from exposure to the sun and from naturally occurring radiation in the limestone bluff. You guys laid right on top of a uranium deposit probably with your shirts off! Now the world doesn't need to know that. The red spots were chigger bites from lying in the grass and not using enough DEET. Understand Sergeant?"

"Yes sir. Thank you. Now it makes sense!" That made no sense as all. What kind of idiot does this guy think I am? That's the biggest load of crap I ever heard!

The doctor babbled on, "I want you to know, both you guys were pretty sick when you came back. Tobias got it worse than you did. We gave you some strong medication. It can cause you to have funny dreams and effect your memory. Even months from now a funny dream might pop up! It's just a side effect from the medication. If you don't discuss them with anyone they'll go away fast."

"Yes sir. I understand." I'm not supposed to discuss my dreams? We must have seen something important. Something secret. They know Toby and I were abducted by aliens along with a score of other poor souls and used as lab rats. That was the only thing that made sense to me.

"Don't mess around with these OSI people either. You hear me sergeant?" the doctor added.

"Yes sir, loud and clear. I understand and thank you sir."

I was discharged from the hospital and sent home with a bucket full of pills along with strict instructions on how to take them. I asked Nurse Debra, "Hey Deb, what the hell are these pills? What are they for?"

She hesitated. "I'm not sure Terry. They aren't from our pharmacy ... they were sent here from Wright Patterson," she said.

I knew Deb well. She wanted to tell me more but chose not to. Rank may have been an issue too. She wore a silver bar on her collar.

Every evening they sent a nurse to our home. Her demeanor was formal, almost businesslike. She never once asked how I felt. It was her job to count the capsules to make sure I had taken my daily dose of nine. Three with each meal. They wanted to be certain I took them as directed.

These were odd generic-looking capsules. I worked in a hospital. I had a recent edition of a Physician's Desk Reference or PDR at home. The book has color photographs of every single capsule approved by the FDA. These capsules weren't listed anywhere! That meant they were specially made by a pharmacist. But from Wright Patterson? What was their purpose? I wish I'd saved just one capsule.

Once I was home, my memory began to suddenly fail me. I couldn't remember the simplest things. I would misplace my watch and a dozen other things out of character for me. Even the day of the week was suddenly a mystery. Sheila was worried about my mental state. Then she made a connection!

Taking the capsules coincided with my rapidly deteriorating memory. I had taken just three of the fourteen days prescribed. Sheila deduced the capsules were the cause of my memory loss! I stopped taking them immediately and only saved enough pills to satisfy the nurse's evening pill-count. I flushed three capsules down the toilet after every meal in case she came early I wanted the pill count to jive. That routine lasted eleven days. My memory improved in a week and fully returned in a month. I wonder if Toby had been poisoned by those capsules.

Our car was returned after just two days. It had been detailed beyond belief. My old Impala had not been so clean since it left the assembly line in Detroit. It had been scrubbed inside and out. We were grateful to have the car back, but I never understood why they took my car? At least not at the time.

A month after my release from the hospital we drove past Toby's house. Not intentionally. We were on our way home from the grocery store and it was the most convenient way home. I was more concerned about running into Toby at the dry cleaners or the grocery store than at his home.

Sheila was driving, and we were two blocks from Toby's house. Despite being ordered to have no contact, I pleaded with Sheila, "Please park so I can say a quick goodbye. I won't be a minute. I promise it'll be okay. I'll be right back."

Sheila was afraid to stop but relented when I begged. She pulled over and parked in front of Toby's house.

"Terry hurry, please hurry," she begged.

There was a moving van in their driveway. Movers were busy hustling in and out with boxes almost at a trot. The front door was wide open.

"Sit tight baby. Everything's fine. I just want a quick goodbye and I'm done." I gave her a peck on the cheek and walked up the short sidewalk to Toby's front door.

Without knocking I walked inside like I'd done a hundred times before. I met Tammy just as she rounded a corner with a lamp in her hand. Surprised, she glared at me with a hard look. "You shouldn't be here!" She kept walking.

She was angry. She probably thought it was my fault they were being uprooted so abruptly. I understood her anger. Maybe she was right. Maybe I'm responsible for whatever happened to Toby and this was all my fault somehow. Maybe that's why it was so important for me to see him one last time.

Toby heard our brief exchange, as he rounded the corner. He was shocked to see me. He looked like hell. An embrace seemed appropriate, but we shook hands. He said, "I guess you heard we're reassigned?"

This moment in my life, those few seconds are in my mind like the birth of my children. Not in a joyous way but it was significant.

"I just want to wish you goodbye. I… wish you good luck…"

Toby looked me in the eye and said very softly, "Do you remember? Did it all really happen Terry, all of it?"

Before I could answer Toby's, question Tammy brushed past us in the hallway again. I'm certain she intentionally interrupted our conversation.

I broke from his gaze and looked down at my shoes. Toby smelled of alcohol and his eyes were bloodshot. His question shook me to my core. Just seeing Toby again and hearing his voice triggered anxiety. I felt my heart pounding in my chest. I wanted to turn and run.

I knew what I had to say, and I owed him that much. I told him, "Yeah, it really happened Tobe, all of it and they hurt us… I don't know why. But it's real my brother. You're not going mad."

That was it. I never re-engaged his eyes. I turned and stumbled back to the car without looking back.

That was the last I would ever see of Toby. I had no way to know what lay ahead for him. Strangely, while I was attending law school 45 minutes away Toby was dying on the streets of Flint, Michigan. Had I known, maybe I could have done something. Survivor's guilt?

I wish we could have reconnected. But Toby wasn't to be found. Sometimes people choose not to be found. Toby had vanished.

As I exited Toby's front door, I was horrified to see that two security policemen in a marked car were parked out front. I had been inside for less than four minutes! They were parked right on our ass, too! There was a pick-up truck parked in front of us, so they had us boxed in. I hopped in the car. Sheila was in a panic and crying.

"What should I do? Oh my God, Terry they're going to arrest us!"

"No way. We'd be in handcuffs right now if they wanted us! You're going to calm down. You're a good driver, this is no worse than parking in downtown St. Louis. Just take your time and wiggle out of this space. Take us home, baby, you can do this. Just remember to be calm. They are still in their car. Just take a slow deep breath and you can do this."

I wasn't about to ask the cops to back up! When I saw their faces in the mirror, they were laughing at us!

Now calmer, Sheila slowly extracted us. She went forward and back couple times and then we were free. We drove home. Our house was only a few blocks from Toby's.

The two cops rode our ass all the way home. They were literally inches from our rear bumper. Careful not to exceed the posted 20 mph speed limit, we crawled home. She hit her blinker and we pulled into the driveway. Sheila let out an audible sigh.

The cops parked at the curb directly in front of our house. They watched us.

I grabbed the groceries while Sheila unlocked the front door. I could hear the phone ringing. I dropped the groceries on the kitchen table and I grabbed the phone.

"Hello."

"Hi Sergeant Lovelace! This is Special Agent Gregory with the Office of Special Investigations." He sounded uncharacteristically pleasant.

"Yes sir."

"Well, you just couldn't do it could you? You had to risk it all and violate a direct order from a superior officer. Violating an order is a serious offense, son. It really pisses me off when someone in uniform disobeys an order of mine!"

"I'm sorry sir!" I wondered if the guys in the police car out front were going to arrest me. Maybe arrest both of us.

"You're just dying to exchange uniforms, aren't you?"

"Exchange uniforms? I don't understand, sir."

"Do you prefer your blue uniform, or would you like to exchange it for something with black and white stripes?"

"No sir?" It took a second or two for his words to register. Then I knew what he meant. He was talking about a prison uniform.

"Son, what did you and Tobias talk about? What did you give him to keep for you? Did you find that other camera yet?"

"No sir, and nothing sir."

"Watch your ass, Lovelace. We're watching yours. I think you need a new hobby. Instead of photography how about stamp collecting? That would suit you."

Then he just hung up!

The security policemen sat in front of our home for about an hour. Then they left. Thankfully, nothing ever came of it. But every day afterward, I faced the worry of being arrested.

After the phone call from Gregory, I realized this whole thing was eating me up inside. I thought maybe if I offered to take a polygraph test, we could end this thing! I had nothing to hide, at least as far as a second camera and film. I hadn't photographed the things we saw. I didn't know it at the time, but it was a stupid idea that likely would have cost me dearly.

I fumbled through my wallet and found Agent Gregory's business card.

I called him expecting to get the switchboard, but my call went right to his desk. He answered on the first ring. "This is Special Agent Gregory."

"Good morning sir this is Staff Sergeant Lovelace. I just had a thought sir. I could take a lie-detector test for you! Sir, I can prove I haven't hidden anything or done anything wrong except going into the …"

True to form Special Agent Gregory cut me off. He was blunt, "You got some film for me yet? I'm waiting?"

I didn't answer.

"Otherwise there's nothing to talk about. The clocks ticking son and I got my own lie detector!" He must have slammed the receiver down. The conversation only raised my anxiety.

Recuperating at home gave me time to rest. At Sheila's urging, I sat down and journaled everything that had happened. I began with the start of the camping idea. Bits and pieces of my memory faded a little each day and it was a struggle to get everything on paper. It was a race to get it all down before it evaporated. It was difficult to grab a pen and paper when I just woke up from a nightmare screaming. I wasn't as disciplined as I thought. It was my wife's patient but firm resolve to see that whatever I saw in the dream made its way into the journal. Sometimes it was only images. I drew them as best I could.

Then it was time to return to work. I reported to my new duty station on time and looking my best. I was pleased that my new commanding officer seemed like a reasonable guy, as officers go. He said, "We don't have a spot for you as a medic. We're a support unit. But our first sergeant's a good man. He'll keep you busy."

"Yes sir, may I ask where I'll be assigned?

"That will be up to Roy. Around here our first sergeant is known as Roy. Also, I am lifting your travel restriction effective immediately."

"Thank you, sir!" That was good news at least.

I was dismissed. I strolled down the hallway to the door marked, "First Sergeant, Roland Gilbert." I'd prefer Roy over Roland any day. I knocked once and was told to enter. His office was closet size. He introduced himself as, "First Sergeant Gilbert." Okay, I'll call the guy First Sergeant Gilbert until he tells me otherwise.

He was a rail thin man. His expressions and mannerisms could best be described as "cold fish." He was anything but welcoming. I wasn't expecting a welcome party. But I didn't expect to be treated like a pariah either. He told me I'd be working the day shift.

I guess since I had declined to reenlist, I would spend the rest of my time counting days on my calendar and drinking coffee. Anyone who has ever served in the armed forces knows how important coffee is to the overall running of things.

My new co-workers avoided me like a leper. Roy was sure to assign me to a task that kept me isolated from the rest of the squadron.

Sounding chipper now, Roy said, "Lovelace, I have a few things that need to be done. Follow me."

Without a word we walked outside. Behind the main facility was a large garage. It was once used as a workshop of some kind. There was an old wood lathe in a corner and still sawdust on the floor. It had been a carpentry shop at one time. But it looked like it had been abandoned since the Korean War.

Handing me a key he said, "Here is your key to the kingdom. Don't lose it. Lovelace, see that stack of plywood there?"

"Yes, I see it." Damn I wasn't blind, and I hated being addressed by last name.

"I need you to spray paint thirty 4x8 foot sheets of plywood. Paint both sides. Use the white paint in the corner and take your time. Do a good job."

I didn't question the purpose. My instructions continued.

"Lovelace, you can take an hour for lunch between noon and 1:00 p.m. Lock up while you're gone. At 4:30 you can call it a day and go home. I'm very busy. Let me know when you're done. Otherwise I don't need to hear from you, understood? Just come and go as needed inside the shop. If you have any questions, now is the time to address them?"

"No sergeant. I think I got it."

Unbelievable. I was an exceptional EMT with skills learned by years of experience in the field. There were any number of productive things I could do. Now I'm painting plywood? Maybe it was because I had Agent Gregory still on my ass? It didn't make sense. I'd come to expect things not to make sense.

The spray paint was old and very low quality. It took several coats of paint to cover the bare wood. It took weeks. When I was finished, and everything was dry, I reported to the first sergeant's office. I knocked on Roy's door.

"Lovelace! Come in. How's your project coming?" he asked.

"I wrapped it up today. Would you like to see?" I asked.

"Oh yeah let's go see what they look like." His enthusiasm was disingenuous.

He walked with me in silence to the workshop. After 10 minutes of inspection he pointed out a spot or two where the paint had run. It really was insignificant.

"Very good, Lovelace. Not too bad."

"Thanks sergeant. Do you have anything else I could do for the unit? Hopefully something a little more cerebral?"

He pretended to think for a moment, rubbing his chin, "Yes, yes I do! Now strip them down to bare wood. Sand paper is on the workbench." He turned and walked away!

I understood him loud and clear.

Hypnosis

Two months later I was still in my workshop and diligently sanding away the same paint I had so carefully applied weeks earlier. I began to enjoy the privacy and now considered the old garage to be, "my workshop." I was surprised one day to see the first sergeant drop by to visit. That was a first. But he didn't come into the shop. He just yelled at me through an open door.

"Hey Lovelace! The CO wants to see you right away. Lock up here before you go."

Asking me to lock up the shop before leaving was troubling. That meant I'd be gone somewhere for a while. It was not a good sign. I locked up the shop and made a quick stop to take a leak. I looked in the mirror to check my appearance then ran down the hallway to his office. His secretary was waiting for me. She motioned me to go in.

"Sergeant Lovelace. Reporting as ordered sir."

His office was decorated with the usual war souvenirs and self-aggrandizing photographs and awards. The tone of his voice was pleasant enough.

"Stand at ease Sergeant Lovelace. They want to see you at OSI headquarters. They've sent a car for you. It should be at the front entrance by now. I suggest that you don't keep them waiting. You are dismissed."

I made a quick exit.

This would be either very good or very bad. Breaking into a run, I headed down the long corridor to the front door. There was a dark blue squad car pulling up to the front stairs.

The driver opened the car's back door for me. He never said a word during the ten-minute ride to OSI Headquarters.

This was my first and last time in the back of a police car. I noticed there were no doorknobs, window cranks, or locks. The floor was steel with two metal rings bolted to the floor. I imagined they must be for securing shackled prisoners. The thought was chilling. The car smelt vaguely of vomit and that pine scented floor cleaner the hospital uses. The ride did nothing to ease my sense of dread.

The driver parked the car at the front entrance. Opening my door, he said, "Follow me."

We went up a few stairs and we were "buzzed in" through a pair of heavy steel doors. They made a metallic "click" when unlocked and again as they closed behind us. The place was intimidating. It was painted drab grey and muted pastels with very few windows. The building looked like something Stalin would design. Even the architecture was intimidating.

We made a right turn and walked down another long corridor. The hallway was lined with steel doors on each side. He opened the door of room "D" with a key.

"Someone will be with you shortly." The metal door shut like a bank vault. I didn't try the knob. I knew it was locked.

Looking around, I did my best to take in everything. The room was maybe 14 x 14 and painted beige. In the middle of the room sat a steel military issue desk from the 50s, and a matching heavy padded chair. Three light fiberglass chairs were placed in the corners for a total of four.

I sat in the padded chair and looked around. The steel door had a small glass window about 5 x 7 inches square. It was made of thick glass and reinforced with crisscrossed wires. An electric clock hung on the wall above the door. To my left was a two-foot square mirror. I reasoned the mirror had to be a two-way affair. Who'd care about grooming enough to need a mirror in a holding cell? I wanted to look at it closely. I wondered what I'd see if I'd cup my hands to block out the light and looked in. I didn't think it wise.

I made myself comfortable and took note that it was now 9:15 AM. I was scared and anxious. I was ever so thankful I stopped to piss before the ride over.

Not a single soul passed in front of my little window. That seemed unusual. Then hours passed. It was 10:00 and then 11:00. I believe the wait was intentional.

At last, just a few minutes before noon, I had company. The door opened, and I recognized Agent Gregory and the captain. There was no apology for making me wait. No civility. As usual they were just all business. The door locked behind them.

I don't believe they said a single word to me. Other than to make me surrender my comfortable chair in exchange for one of the fiberglass ones.

Gregory finally spoke to me. He was civil if not pleasant. "Well, have you found any film for us?"

"No sir. I don't have any," I said.

"It doesn't matter anymore. If you cooperate today, we might just close your file. Would you like that?"

I said, "Yes sir, whatever I can do to put this matter behind me."

"We should be done in a couple hours," Gregory replied.

A couple hours! I thought to myself. What the hell are we going to talk about for hours? I noticed their little tape recorder was being set-up by the captain again. It was on the table, but the little wheels weren't turning yet. Agent Gregory pulled a manila folder from his briefcase. He retrieved a piece of paper out and handed it to me.

He told me to read it to myself silently first. Then I would read it out loud for the recorder. I read the paper silently. It was a rehash of the forms I'd signed in the hospital. Most of it was to waive whatever rights I had. Also, that I agreed my statements were made knowingly and voluntarily. The captain switched on the reel-to-reel.

Gregory asked me, "Are you ready to read it for the record now?"

I nodded.

He rolled his eyes and tapped the tape recorder with his pen. Its wheels were turning. I knew what he wanted.

We started over. "Sergeant Lovelace, you may begin when you're ready. Keep your voice up okay? Go ahead."

Script in hand I began, "I agree under penalty ... the Uniform Code of Military Justice ..."

I was on autopilot again. I was simply processing written words. I spoke mechanically. I was careful to enunciate each word but without processing it fully for content. I didn't read it for substance. These were just words falling out of my mouth. Like spray-painting plywood boards.

As soon as I was finished, Gregory said a few words into the recorder. He began "This is Special Agent Gregory ...." He stated my name and gave the date and time, a file number, etc.

Then Gregory addressed me again, "Sergeant Lovelace, has anyone mistreated you or physically harmed you in any way?"

"No sir," I was quick to reply.

"Has anyone threatened you or promised you anything in exchange for your statements today?"

"No sir."

With that, he turned off the recorder and we sat! We were waiting for something. It was a short wait.

243

The men went about their business as if they were preparing for another person to join us. They shuffled papers and whispered back and forth. The topic was fishing.

Gregory said to me casually, "You're going to be hypnotized today and administered some medicine to help you remember everything clearly."

"Medication! Sir, what kind of medication? Sir but why? I told you everything and I don't have any film!"

He glared at me. Pulling a piece of paper from his briefcase he slammed it down on the table in front of me. With his index finger he pointed, "Is that not your signature, son?"

"Yes sir, just why...?"

"This is all the *why* I need." Gregory then slid it into his briefcase. He nodded to the captain and the tape recorder was running again.

Now I was really frightened. I thought about withdrawing my consent or asking for a lawyer. But I knew those options carried risks. I didn't trust these guys. I violated Gregory's "no contact order" when I stopped by Toby's house. I committed a trespass too. I knew I was screwed.

I decided to ask, "Do you guys think I saw something secret?"

That question didn't register at all. The room fell silent. I think it was because the tape recorder was running again. They ignored my question completely. Both men scribbled on their legal pads.

A few minutes later a major tapped on the little glass window. The captain was closest to the door and let him in. He wore golden oak leaves but no nametag. I'd never seen him before. He carried a little kit with him. It looked like a shaving kit made of leather.

This major shook hands with the agents. It was obvious they knew one another. He then made Gregory relinquish his padded chair in exchange for a fiberglass one. He must carry more authority than Gregory. He glanced at the tape recorder to be sure it was running.

In deference to the major, the two agents pulled back from the table. The major pulled his chair next to mine. He encroached on my space. Even though he wore a broad smile, he was intimidating.

I wondered who the hell is this guy? Is he the hypnotist?

Once everyone had settled, he shook my hand warmly. With eye contact and that broad smile, he introduced himself with enthusiasm. "Hi, Sergeant Lovelace! It's very nice to finally meet you! I'm Major Brownfield!"

He carried himself more like a therapist or a priest than a military officer.

"But just today you can call me Brad instead of Major Brownfield. Won't you please? That is my name!"

I took that to be an order and not a suggestion. He continued, "Sergeant, just for our little visit today, can I call you Terry instead of Sergeant Lovelace?" He maintained eye contact and never stopped smiling.

"Yes sir, of course." I replied.

Smiling, he softly scolded me for calling him "sir." He asked, "Don't you mean, yes Brad?"

"Sorry, yes Brad." It was weird speaking to a major so casually while in uniform.

"Tell me a little about yourself, where are you from?" he asked.

Then began a pleasant conversation. He claimed to know folks in St. Louis. He rattled off a few landmarks. I sensed he was seeking common ground.

When I spoke, he listened politely and kept his smile. He nodded now and then when appropriate. This polite chitchat went back and forth for a good while.

He actual did put me at ease a little! I learned that a kind human voice has an impact on people. Especially on people stressed or scared.

Even in this confined environment I didn't feel like I was being interrogated, not yet at least. Not by Brad. But I knew things would soon change.

Brad feigned a genuine interest in everything I had to say. After a while, that began to make me uneasy. My life just wasn't that interesting. He must have sensed my discomfort and abruptly switched gears.

"Terry, do you trust me?"

That question took me by surprise. Feeling caught off guard I gave the courteous albeit untruthful answer, "Yes Brad, I trust you."

"Good. You can trust me Terry. That's very good."

The whole exchange just felt creepy. We talked for another ten minutes about photography and cameras. I began to feel weirdly comfortable with him again. It was like I knew this guy from somewhere. But mentally I knew it was time to put my guard up. I didn't want to be disarmed by kind words.

While we were talking, he opened his leather kit. He laid a little towel on the table and meticulously arranged the contents of his kit on the towel. He wanted things arranged just so. What caught my eye was a hypodermic syringe already loaded with a yellow fluid. I thought it could be sodium pentothal or something of the like. The stuff you hear in movies referred to as, "truth serum."

He continued to smile and began humming softly to himself. There was a blood pressure cuff with stethoscope, alcohol swabs, and a bandage. There was also a foot-long piece of rubber tubing to use as a tourniquet to locate a vein. Whatever that yellow stuff was, it was intended for me.

"Terry, have these gentlemen explained to you we're going to hypnotize you today? You signed a consent form to undergo investigative hypnosis. It's a common tool."

"Yes sir, Brad. But why?"

"It's no big deal, Terry! Hypnosis can help you relax and help you to remember details that you might have forgotten."

I didn't reply. It was like the guy read my mind!

Brad stopped smiling and his voice turned ominous, "Are you thinking about withdrawing your consent now?"

"No sir, no Brad."

Still wearing his stern affect the major added, "Hypnosis will tell us if you're intentionally holding back information. Now, you wouldn't do that, would you Terry?"

"I wouldn't, Brad. I won't lie to you or to the agents."

"Terry, listen if there's anything in your statement that you want to change or if there's anything you've held back because it slipped your mind, we can fix it. Tell me now and we might just be done here today!"

"Brad, I told the agents everything I know," I answered.

"Terry, this is your opportunity to finish this. If you need to make any corrections to your statement, it's a lot better to just tell me now and I can help you. Terry, this will end very badly for you if you've been lying to Agent Gregory. I'll ask these two gentlemen to step outside and we can have a private talk, whada-ya, say, hmm?"

The two agents stood.

"Sir, I told them everything truthfully."

The two agents sat back down.

I had no option but to roll with it. But was determined—, I was determined to resist giving him full control of my mind. I would passively and covertly resist his hypnosis.

I thought I could keep a little compartment in my mind segregated, separate. I tried to establish boundaries in my mind. I would wall off an area for the interrogation and an area for my conscious resistance. I won't let him hypnotize me! I told myself. I would resist but I knew I had to appear compliant at the same time.

Pushing the envelope, I spoke up one more time. "Now I understand the hypnosis Brad, but what's the injection for?"

The major raised his voice. Both agents jumped! He took on the stern affect again, "My goodness! For someone who claims to trust me you sure have a lot of questions!" He turned the smile back on, "Terry, it's just to help you relax. It makes the hypnosis process quicker and more effective. You'll feel like you've had a couple beers. It will help you to fully relax so you can remember things easily. Who knows? Maybe you'll remember something important that you forgot."

I didn't respond.

"Terry I've done these a hundred times and I promise you, this won't hurt a bit."

The discussion was over. He reached over and took my left arm. Humming all the while he unbuttoned my shirtsleeve and rolled it up. With the rubber tubing tightly around my bicep, he began looking for a vein.

I watched him go about his business. I was more curious than afraid.

Chipper than ever Brad said, "In a few seconds I'm going to give you a little injection in your arm here. I promise it won't hurt. It's very much like the medication they gave you while you were in the hospital. Now, do you still trust me Terry?"

I lied, "Yes Brad."

"Good!" He took the cap off the syringe and held it in his right hand. "Now Terry, we've only just met but I promise you I'm not going to hurt you in any way. A lot of people tell me they enjoy this experience. I bet you're a guy who enjoys a few beers on occasion." He followed up with another wink of his eye.

I said nothing. I was insulted. Not all enlisted guys drink.

"Just sit back now and listen to my voice. It's important that you don't resist the feeling. Let the medicine do its job. Obey the commands I give you and we'll be done before you know it. Will you do that for me Terry?"

I had to reply aloud, "Yes Brad. I promise." I thought oh shit, he's going to give me a hypnotic suggestion to obey his commands. I'd been taking evening classes in psychology for two years now. I knew a little about hypnosis and hypnotic suggestion. I knew it was possible to resist but the drug concerned me. I thought, if it were possible to drug a person into revealing the truth why would we need courts of law and trials? That thought gave me hope.

"Terry, have you ever been hypnotized before?"

"No Brad."

I had some things to hide. But I sure as hell wasn't hiding any film. Some memories were so incredible I wanted to keep them to myself for fear they'd think I'm insane. Those incredible things I saw. I owned them, and I held onto them as validation. It was like when I tucked the curtain inside the venetian blinds in 1966. I didn't want to be robbed of the experience. Even if it was a bad experience. I owned those images the same way I owned my photographs. They were mine.

"You have a good vein here," he mumbled while he smacked the crook of my arm a couple times.

The major had a voice like a radio announcer, smooth and easy to listen to. He found a vein and scrubbed it with an alcohol swab. He cautioned, "Here we go. A little sting," smiling all the while.

"Listen to my voice Terry and forget about everything else now and just relax ... relax."

I didn't feel a thing. Peeking through my mostly closed left eye I watched the needle pierce my arm. After he stuck me he pulled back the plunger. A bit of blood backed up into the syringe. He had hit a vein.

I think Brad saw my eyelids flutter as I was peeking at the needle.

"Close your eyes now Terry. Relax and keep your eyes shut and listen to my voice. That's better; you have good veins. Thank you, Terry!"

Strange that someone would complement the quality of my veins. I felt obliged to reply in kind. "You're welcome Brad." I noticed the silence in the room. The agents were uncharacteristically quiet.

I heard "snap" and felt him remove the rubber tourniquet. I felt a flush and then warmth as my muscles involuntarily relaxed. Brad was correct. It was a pleasant feeling.

"There, all done. Terry, that wasn't so bad, was it?" He placed a bandage on my arm.

I slid from feeling relaxed into feeling sedated. The acoustics in the room abruptly changed. This was not at all the same drug they gave me in the hospital! This was something very different.

"Terry, you're just going to feel a little sleepy, but you don't want to fall asleep. You want to listen to my voice. You're in a safe place. You feel warm and comfortable now."

At that instant I felt another wave of warmth wash over my body. I didn't feel like I was in that safe place though! I also reaffirmed in my mind that I would passively resist surrendering to Brad's voice.

I didn't "feel" hypnotized yet. I just felt sedated. His voice was well, hypnotic. I kept playing Beatles songs in my head. I did anything I could think of to avoid surrendering total control.

I didn't know how one was supposed to feel under hypnosis. But I didn't feel like I imagined one would feel. I'd seen people hypnotized on television programs using "stage hypnosis." I thought, I can mimic that kind of behavior, sleepy and robotic-like.

He continued in his monotone voice. "You're safe now Terry and we're going to go back in time together just to look around. I'll be right beside you. Would that be alright with you?"

"Okay Brad, yes." I let my head droop to my chest and kept my eyes closed.

"Now listen carefully Terry and do as I say. I'm going to count out loud down from ten to one. I want you to imagine a stairway in your mind. Can you see a stairway leading down to a cellar?"

"Yes Brad," I did have a mental image of a stairway.

"With each number I count, you'll take one step down on those ten imaginary stairs. You'll feel more and more relaxed with each step. You'll be relaxing more and more, more with every step you take as you listen to my voice. Just listen to my voice. Okay Terry? Here we go."

He began his countdown.

"Take that first step Terry and feel relaxed. With each step you take you'll feel twice as relaxed. You're warm and safe. I won't let anything hurt you."

The idea occurred to me as Brad's count continues downward, I can mentally count upward! I'll go the opposite direction on the number line. I'd climb up the stairs on the number line instead. I guess math class was good for something. I tried it mentally. It was the best idea I could come up with.

Brad continued, "Take the second step now twice as relaxed. You are relaxed and at ease, warm and secure."

I made the conscious effort to not relax all my body. Intentionally, I tightened the muscles in my toes and other parts of my body where he wouldn't notice I had tensed. I knew I needed to appear relaxed. But the smooth tone of his voice made me want to listen to him. I knew that was the danger, giving him my full attention.

We continued our opposite journeys on the stairway. "You're doing well Terry. We're all very proud of you. Feeling eight times more relaxed now."

In my mind's eye, when he called off a step, I mentally took a step in the opposite direction on the mental stairway. I was headed away from that dark cellar. I'll stay upstairs in the light thank you very much!

I finished my count at #1 as he finished his count at #10. I was relaxed but conscious of my surroundings. I was aware of everything going on around me. But I felt very sedated.

"Ten! You're at the bottom now. Terry, above you there's a chain hanging down from the ceiling. I want you to reach up with your right arm and pull it downward to turn on the light, so we can look around. Do it now Terry."

My arm didn't move on its own accord. I had complete control of my arm. I wasn't sure what to do. A few tense moments passed.

Brad tried again, "Terry reach up now. Take the chain and pull it to turn on that light so we can look around a little."

This time I intentionally reached up with my right arm and made a motion like I was pulling a chain. I was pulling a chain alright. I was pulling Brad's chain. I then lowered my arm into my lap.

"It's brightly lit now, you're not in the darkness and you're very safe. Listen to my voice and relax Terry."

I heard the captain whisper, "I'm amazed every time I watch this!"

After a few minutes of whispering back and forth I heard Agent Gregory ask in a whisper, "Is he under?"

The major replied, "Oh yeah, piece of cake … he was under before I hit three."

The captain chuckled.

I thought, so the captain is amazed every time he watches one of these? Damn, how many people do they hypnotize? They can't do this with everyone who sees a UFO? But my interaction was a little more intimate. I had established a dialogue with at least one alien being. I could see her clearly in my mind now. This is a familiar memory but one I hadn't thought about in a very long time. The medicine opened a doorway. It was as if you were trying to remember a word or phrase and someone gives you a hint. Then boom! You remember. I was remembering.

There was some hushed talk between the three about golf. I guess the major didn't fish. I was stunned. Surely, I wasn't supposed to hear this conversation.

The major asked one of the agents, "Let me review his cover sheet really quick." There was a shuffling of paper and a minute later I heard Brad say, "Alright, I got it, thanks Greg."

Brad turned his attention back to me. "Terry, you can hear my voice. Do you feel nice and relaxed now? Okay, we're going to take that little trip back in time like I promised. Just to look around."

"Yes Brad," I answered, anxious as hell.

"Good. You're a very good subject! You're the best subject I've seen in a while!"

I just said, "Thank you." Like complimenting me on the quality of the vein in my arm; that must be a part of the process.

That felt eerie! It was awkward. I was in a pleasant twilight though. I was very relaxed but still aware of everything going on around me. It seemed to be working for me to split my mind into two separate compartments. I ran through the lyrics of *Yellow Submarine* and *Norwegian Wood*.

"Now listen to my voice Terry. Do you still trust me?"

"Yes Brad, I trust you." Like hell I thought.

"Terry we're going to go back in time but only in your memory. We are only going there to look around before we get rid of those nasty images. Think of it like watching a movie. It seems real but it's just memories. They are things that happened a long time ago, not dreams or stories, but what you see. I want you to tell me what you see. Let's go back to the meadow. When I tell you to, look around in your mind and tell me what you see."

"Yes Brad."

"Nothing in your memory can hurt you, we are not going to let anything happen to you. I'm right here, and anything that's scary is just a memory."

That made me feel anxious. Sure, there are things I don't want to look at. It's like viewing an autopsy. Ugly and gruesome not something to dwell on or even think about when it's over. Like snakes, some things are best to let lay undisturbed.

Brad could tell I was anxious. He reached out and took my right hand. He said, "Terry, hold my hand. Do you feel my hand?"

"I feel it Brad," it was very strange holding this strange man's hand. But I admit it felt reassuring, too. If they surfaced, I expected there were memories that would be difficult to relive. He wanted me to be ready for the ugly when it came. We both knew it was coming.

Brad spoke to me like I was a child. It seemed weirdly appropriate at the time. I was beginning another song in my mind. It was playing in that private compartment where I maintained control.

"Now I want you to think back. Do you remember taking a camping trip? Did you and Tobias go on a little camping trip?"

"Yes Brad, its Toby not Tobias. We went on a camping trip."

"Of course, you did. That's right! You and Toby went to Devils Den. My, that must have been exciting! Tell me about your trip. Think hard and tell me what you see."

Throughout the entire interrogation I felt conscious but very drowsy. There were times when I fell asleep for just a second or two only to have Brad pull me back.

I told Brad my edited version of the story. I told him about the drive, the girl in the store and crossing the chained area .... arriving at the meadow. How we chose a place to park in the meadow, the hike and falling asleep on the ledge. I told him about our mad dash to get back to the campsite before sundown. I gave a detailed account easily because I could watch it play out in my mind in sequence of events. It truly was like watching a motion picture in your head.

"That's good Terry. I want you to tell me what you saw in the sky, if anything, when it got dark."

"Brad, there were three stars. We watched them travel from the horizon until they were directly over our heads. We were parked in the right spot..."

I must have been prattling-on. There were times that I may have been under or asleep. Brad dragged up things from my subconscious mind. These were either things I had forgotten or things they repressed.

These were the ugly things. Some of these things will sound outrageous I know. But in the introduction to this book I promised I would tell you the truth. This is the truth. These were my objective experiences. Nothing here is subjective. I don't draw any conclusions.

Brad broke into my thought. "Tell me Terry, how did you know just where to go?"

For some odd reason that question hit me like a slap in the face. "Brad, they told Toby where we should go. He knew right where to go. Toby knew. They didn't tell me, just Toby."

"Who was it Terry? Who told Toby where to go?"

Without hesitation I spat out, "The space people did."

Did that just come out of my mouth! I was answering questions before thinking about my answer! I remembered the space people now! I had all but forgotten so much. I had forgotten a hell of a lot.

Here is where things get fuzzy. I'm aware and can hear my spoken responses to his questions. I don't recall thinking about the answers before they came out of my mouth. I tried to keep the door to the other compartment in my mind open by playing song after song mentally. I resisted with everything I had. But I felt a piece of me slip away now and then. Resisting hypnosis was very possible. Battling the effects of the drug was another matter altogether.

I told Brad, "Yes, in the meadow. Toby knew right where to park."

Brad paused, "Tell me all about getting to the meadow."

"We found the correct spot to camp. It was on the edge of the meadow. We couldn't go to a public campsite. We had to be up high on the plateau because that's where they land."

"Good Terry. Tell me everything that happened that night. Did they take you and Toby together?"

"Yes and no Brad. They took me twice. Toby slept through the first time on the rock ledge where we stopped to rest. Then they took me again late at night when they took me for a second time with Toby. They took blood from me and my sperm too. They have a machine they put over my genitals and bam! It's humiliating but it was no good to resist them. They had us Brad."

I was seeing this play-out in my mind. It was all familiar. These were real and terrifying memories suppressed by the aliens. I knew there was some scary shit coming too. I had to appear relaxed but hold onto my grasp of consciousness. Now, I wanted to know what happened to us on that goddamn meadow. All of it.

I was quiet for a moment. Brad didn't like it. He pressed me.

"Ah, Terry you and Toby saw some lights in the sky. Didn't you see some stars too? How many stars did you see?"

"Stars… three stars that formed a triangle. We watched them from where they sat on the horizon and followed them. We watched them go all the way up until they were right over our heads. The closer it got, the bigger it got… and it was very big."

"Terry, did you know who it was? Who was in the meadow to visit you that night?"

"I told you Brad. It was the space people." I was annoyed. Here is where I must have dozed off for a moment. There are gaps in the story here that I can't account for.

"Yes Brad, the space people. They wanted both of us this time. They hurt us too. They hurt me badly and they hurt Toby even worse. Much worse. I heard his screams."

Brad asked, "Tell me about the space people."

"I already knew the space people. I knew them before this night. I remember in the tent, Toby's voice saying to me, 'It was the space people, they took you too!' I remember. I said, 'Yeah Toby. They took us both.' They took me when I was a little kid too. It was the monkeymen."

Brad was intrigued, "Terry, who are the monkeymen?"

Fear overtook me. I could see them clearly now! I saw them in my mind's eye. I softly sobbed as I saw the monkeymen for the first time unmasked." These were no friendly little monkeys. These were non-human entities disguised to fool a child and put them at ease.

"Brad, I know them. They came into my bedroom when I was little. They took me somewhere and there were toys and other children for me to play with. There was a lady there who was nice." I squeezed the major's hand. I knew I wasn't in danger, but all the emotions were there. I felt the same panic.

"Terry, you're safe. I'm right here. Now go on, continue."

I was reliving the horror of an alien abduction. It was both terrifying and familiar. I've known these space people all my life! I never thought of it that way before!

I told Brad, "They were the monkeymen from my childhood and they follow me. They always know where to find me. You can't hide from them."

"Terry what do the monkeymen look like? Why do you call them monkeymen?"

"What an asinine question Brad!" I shouted out loud. "Because they looked like little monkeys. There were four of them and they all wore masks. I can see them now; their masks are off. These aren't monkeys at all. These are the little grey people. They took me! They took me to play when I was little. Oh, God help me. I am so afraid of them. I can see their evil grin. They tricked me!"

"Okay Terry, stay focused. Go back to the tent. What happened to you and Toby in the tent? Tell me what you saw?"

"We were taken from the tent,"

Brad asked, "You and Tobias saw the stars first? Then the triangle and what did you see next?"

"We watched the ship come in from just three little lights. It climbed up and over us. God, it was so big. But we weren't afraid. Toby wasn't scared either. We just went to sleep. We were so tired, and we just weren't interested," I was reliving the whole thing in my mind and it was terrifying.

I could hear the major addressing the two agents, "I've seen this dozens of times before. There is alien apathy and alien amnesia. They're two separate phenomena. It's common."

I thought to myself, "alien apathy and alien amnesia" now I get it! It's why I went back to bed as a child with a spaceship parked outside my bedroom window. It's why Toby and I just went to sleep! I must remember this, it is important.

The major resumed the interrogation, "You weren't interested, and you went to bed. What time did you enter your tent that night?"

"Right before their ship docked. It landed in the field about midnight. But it was never on the ground. It stayed about thirty feet over the meadow floor. Brad, it just hung there," I said as I watched it all play out in my head. I was amazed at the images I saw, but they were familiar too. It was like seeing an old friend you'd not seen in years.

Brad said, "Terry, tell me about the spaceship in the meadow. What did it look like? What did you see?"

"A giant triangle of a spaceship. It was hundreds of feet across. It was huge, it was so incredible, I can see it now!" It was as fresh in my mind as what I had for breakfast. It was right there. I wanted to remember it and watch it some more. I paused. I saw it all again and I wanted to imprint it in my memory forever! I said, "It was right there, and it was so big! It filled the meadow like a five-story building."

"Good Terry. That must have been exciting for you! Tell me about the ship. When they took you and you were inside with Toby, what did you see inside?"

"Incredible things. This had to be one of their bigger ones," I added almost as a matter-of-fact.

My conscious mind stopped playing the music. It dawned on me. He knows all about them already! He is spot on with everything! It was no star! The son of a bitch knew it was no star, it was a goddamn spaceship. How did he know? How could he know? He's leading me down a path to find out how much I know.

"Go on Terry, you're doing well now what did you see?"

I spoke again without first composing my thoughts, "It was a big ship Brad, a large one. It was different than the flying saucers and the giant ship I saw before. It wasn't silver, and it wasn't shiny. It was matte finish I'd call it and very dark grey or black. Kind of like the black diamond we saw over Kilo-5. It had lights on each corner that ran from the bottom to the top."

"Go on Terry," Brad encouraged.

I was agitated again, "Brad these space people capture me and do terrible things to me ... and then make erase my memory. It happened when I was a little boy. But it wasn't just two times either. Oh God they took me. They took me lots of times and made me forget it all. But they wanted me to remember just a little when I was a kid. So, I would recognize them when I grew up. I was programmed to see them as my space brothers and I had to keep their secret."

"Good Terry." There was a pause and shuffling of papers.

As a prosecutor, I learned how child molesters "groom" their victims. They ingratiate themselves into the victim's families to gain their trust. It took until now for the mask of my abusers to come down. I had been groomed. Those were terrifying but brief encounters in my childhood. But they were not nearly as brief as I remembered. They damaged my soul the way a child molester robs children of their innocence. There was so much I'd forgotten until Brad came along. He brought all this out again. He ripped the scab off my wound.

The drugs he gave me, and his faulty hypnosis brought it all back into my conscious mind. It was a eureka moment for me. An epiphany. I kept it to myself. What else has happened to me that I'm not even aware of? I heard someone once say, "You don't know what you don't know." I never understood the meaning of the phrase until that moment.

Suddenly, I was angry with Brad. I was really pissed-off! I tried not to let it show. I spoke up, "There are some things we're not supposed to talk about, Brad! I'm not supposed to talk about them. You know that! It's a secret and there are consequences if you disobey them. They'll make us both pay! We're in danger now!"

That caused quite a stir. Evidently Brad's the one asking questions and my commentary wasn't appreciated. Brad shot back quickly and reassuringly to calm me down and take back his role as the inquisitor, "No, no it's alright! They gave us permission! Terry you're safe now. They won't be mad at you! I promise! They said it was alright for me to talk to you."

This attempt to calm me down had the opposite effect. He had permission? Who, in the chain of command gave him the authority to speak on behalf of the aliens? A USAF major had permission? That shook me up. I didn't believe it at first because it was so incredible. I felt myself slipping again. Mentally, I busied half of my mind with Brad while the other half was reciting the multiplication tables. Trying to hold onto a piece of consciousness.

Brad interrupted my thoughts, "Wake up! Stay focused on the triangle. Terry, tell me what you're seeing now."

"Brad, I told you. It was a big, goddamn triangle. As big as the whole goddamn meadow. That's why we had to park by the tree line, so they had room to park over the meadow."

I must have dozed off again at a critical juncture or at least I think so. My memory of this event is not a seamless narrative.

Brad's voice startled me, "Go on Terry and tell me what you see?"

Disturbed by the unaccountable period, I began again, "It was black and five stories tall. It was enormous. There were three saucers situated inside like planes on a carrier parked below deck. There was a crowd of people too. We're all waiting for our turn on the table. The space people control us. The taller aliens are milling about. They are the ones who control everything. If one of them looks at you it's like being naked. They can see and know everything in your mind. That was the scariest thing, so I avoided looking at them."

"How many humans did you see?"

"Fifty or sixty. A lot of people ... Some of the human beings were crew members! They ignored us."

Tell me terry. Tell me what the human crew members wore?"

"Tan colored flight suits with orange insignias of rank on their shoulders," I said. That created a stir. I heard Gregory say, "Son of a bitch!"

"Terry, you'll forget about the men in tan flight suits. Tell me, where did they take you next?" Gregory wanted to know. In retrospect I think he wanted to shift my focus away from the men dressed in tan.

"They marched us past a long wall of aquariums. I don't want to look at them, so I turn away. They're dreadful things, you know Brad? They do horrible things there," here was the ugly. I knew it was coming.

"Terry, turn your head now and look! Terry, tell me about the aquariums... what do you see?"

"They are big fish tanks. Inside them... I thought they were puppies at first... reptilian lizard-like things floating in pink water. They were ugly with big eyes. One twitched!" I must have screamed.

Brad forced me to look, "Terry! They're images from the past and they can't hurt you now! How many aquariums did you see?"

"A hundred or more aquariums... they cover a whole wall. There is pink water inside and some are bigger. They look like... no, fuck no! These are human beings? How can this be? These can't be living human beings ... they are different. Oh god, they are not like us! One moved again, its head turned toward us, and its eyes blinked! Oh, fuck, no!"

I must have fainted. I was overwhelmed. I felt my heart pounding. In my mind I turned away and tried to think of other things. I tried to think about good things like flowers, butterflies, Norwegian wood, the love of my wife and things of beauty. Not these goddamn monsters that Brad made me see again.

I heard the familiar zzzzzzzip, of a blood pressure cuff. Brad was taking my blood pressure and reminding me, "Terry, you're here now and you're safe. That was in the past. Squeeze my hand."

I squeezed Brad's hand and just like before, I felt grounded again. I felt safe. I'm going to remember this for the rest of my life, I swear to God I will! I'm not going to let him rob me of these ugly memories and thoughts. No matter what ... I will not forget this!

Then a disturbing thought. They wouldn't allow a lowly NCO to know about this stuff. So why help me remember? They want to know how much I know... how much I've seen... they want to know if I have photographs too.

I didn't trust these guys. I could be killed in an accident of their design! I could be falsely imprisoned with some made-up story of photographing restricted nuclear facilities or cultivating a marijuana plot in the nature preserve. Any number of things could be engineered to silence me. I remembered the old senile doctor who saw me as I was being discharged from the hospital. He warned me, "Don't mess around with these OSI people." But that was exactly what I was doing, and I was afraid for my life!

"Tell me what happened next, Terry. What else did you see inside the craft?"

"We all walked by the aquariums. Now we're just waiting our turn in a big room. Everything is white or steel. Some people are nude and holding their clothes."

Brad was back in control. The music had stopped playing once more. I was strolling around this spacecraft with a small woman. I could see her. I knew her, and I tried not to tell Brad about her. Maybe I did. Brad asked again, "Tell me about this spacecraft and what you saw."

"I had never seen a triangle before! I've been in their ships before. Even bigger ships. I was inside of one so big it can never land here because it is as big as a city. I was taxied there and back in a saucer. I remember being inside a saucer and it was incredible. We shuttled back and forth in one. They were short trips that only took a couple minutes. There was a slight sensation of motion. It was like being in an elevator."

"Terry, tell me about the biggest one? The one bigger than the triangle. Tell me about that one. But only tell me what you see and what you were told if anything."

I was speaking on autopilot again. I was seeing things play out and then relaying to Brad, "It was an entire city a hundred times larger than the triangle. It was so different. On earth there is a curve, so the horizon is as far as you can see. It's flat inside and I could see as far as my eyesight allowed. The depth of field made it almost like a 3D movie scene. I could make out people walking further away from us. There were probably hundreds of these compartments on either side of a long central corridor. There were golf carts things to move people around. It was like a highway down the center …"

I stopped talking to watch the images play out. Brad didn't like it. But it was captivating I wanted to watch it.

"Terry, tell me what you're see now. Tell me!"

"The tall ones … the aliens are milling about. There are walkways that move like at the airport. We were near the moon that time. There were huge windows and I could see the moon below us! It was dark, but I could see cities below that were lit up. It was a huge city on the surface of the moon! They go there for a special kind of rock."

"Go on Terry. You're doing very well."

"The woman told me they can never fly in front of the moon … the side that faces earth. It's because the ship is so big it could be seen from earth."

"By whom Terry? By people using telescopes?"

"Hell, no Brad! You could see it with two eyes! It would be a black dot travelling across the face of the full moon. Maybe that's why I like the full moon so much, do you think so Brad?"

Brad was struggling to keep me on track, "Who was the woman inside the very big ship, Terry?"

"I don't know her name. We walked together for a while. We talked with our minds. They don't speak but it's easy to communicate. We can hear each other just like we're talking now. She told me the size of the ship but in kilometers. We're supposed to learn metrics now. She told me it was five-hundred and some kilometers-long and seventy-five kilometers tall."

"Did they tell you where they come from? Tell me what she told you?"

"Yes! They stay on the other side of the moon but it's not their real home. It's not where they come from. They come from a place very far away; they have two suns and a couple moons. They never have nighttime so it's easy to grow things there. She told me it was very beautiful. I asked if I could go there but she said it wasn't allowed."

"Did she tell you anything else about our moon?"

"She said we have people living there too! Humans on the moon... for years now. I never knew that Brad. I would never have imagined it!" I said.

That caused a stir. I could hear whispering and pages of paper being flipped.

Brad was quick to jump in, "Very good. Go ahead Terry, but you will forget that memory forever. You'll forget all about the moon, everyone knows there are no people on the moon, Terry. All about the big ship and the moon you will forget. It's gone now!"

I didn't reply. And I don't think I forgot a goddamn thing either. I know what I saw. I remember what she told me.

As if on cue Brad asked, "What else did she tell you?"

I paused, "I… I'm fond of her but not in a romantic way. Like I feel about my friends and people I like. I liked her. She said she was half human and half alien. She said there were a lot of them just like her… and more every day. I felt drawn to her. But my affection for her was maternal. She called me by my name and that helped me to feel more at ease. She was not pretty Brad. But I knew her from before when I was little. She was so kind to me when I was so afraid. We hugged one another. My God… she's so thin and so fragile!"

"What happened after you embraced?" Brad asked.

"The flap of her gown was open a bit and I peeked inside where her breasts would be. I think it's natural curiosity, but… I'm repulsed, it wasn't right Brad. It was not a human body. She was not a human being! It was ugly. She was not a real woman, but I felt fond of her. She talked to me. She kept me from being so scared when I was little, and they hurt me. It was good to see her again. Her kind words helped me to feel less afraid."

I was quiet for a while or there is a big gap here. I don't know which. I recall being startled again by Brad's voice, "Terry, what else did she say to you?"

I was apprehensive again. I knew I was not supposed to talk about this, "Brad, she said I shouldn't tell and she made me forget. Did they really give you permission? Do you know them?"

That seemed to get everybody's attention. I had asked Brad a second question. The topic was off limits, I guessed by their response. Our roles were clearly defined. He was the inquisitor and I was his subject.

There is more hushed whispering. In my mind, I'm still trying to process my encounter with the alien woman. I was shocked and embarrassed that I admitted being fond of her. I was dumbfounded by the things I saw and the things I said. I was still processing the amazing images of her and of being aboard the huge spaceship. So many memories came flooding in… it was overwhelming. I needed to rest for a moment. I felt my heart pounding.

I felt a tightness around my left arm. Brad was checking my blood pressure again. I believe they were freaked out because I had questioned Brad. I needed to remember to not do that in the future, not to tip my hand. But I wasn't always able to control what came out of my mouth. I don't know how much time had lapsed but I was asleep for minutes at least.

"You're a good subject Terry and we're all proud of you. Do you still trust me?" asked Brad.

"I trust you." It came out of my mouth because I forced it to come out. I didn't trust this son of a bitch. I held onto my stubborn resolve not to allow Brad to take total control.

"Terry, we're going to go back one more time okay? Just once more and we'll be done."

I was worried about what I might have said during those moments I couldn't account for. I didn't know what happened during the times I lapsed into sleep or some trance state. The gaps worried me. I was seated away from the clock on the wall. Even if I were facing it I couldn't lift my head to check the time. It felt like an hour had passed. It was more like four.

Brad took me on one more trip, "Okay Terry, you're safe. I want you to go back once more and tell me what you see. What do you see?"

I was emotional. I said, "I was in the tent and I'm screaming. Although I'm not making audible sounds. I fill my lungs with air and screamed again but nothing came out. Everything was silent except for that incredible hum. It was dark except for some bright lights that occasionally flashed outside the tent. Toby was gone."

"Did they take you again Terry?" Brad asked. Of course, he knew they took me again.

"The second time... I was in the tent and the lights were so bright. The humming got louder, then there's that twirling spin. We go right through the tent into the triangle from the center below it. I saw the flash of white light and then I'm in a giant room with other people." I remember a long pause before getting back on topic, "The little grey

274

people are undressing everyone. I was waiting… then they took me into that damned white room. I've been there before Brad. I'm on their table and held down. Then I can't move at all."

Brad wanted to know, "Do they use straps to hold you down to the table?"

"Never, you're just immobile. I didn't know where Toby or the other people went. I could hear a woman screaming now. The sadness of her scream! Brad It was dreadful."

"What do you see happening next Terry?"

I didn't answer. I was just watching the images in my head drift by. I was like a kid thumbing through his favorite deck of baseball cards and absorbed in them.

Brad raised his voice, "Terry, you must speak up. Talk to me and tell me what you see?"

"My body is limp now. I'm still aware of others around me. They are aliens not people. The little grey ones are strong. An alien is always supervising. He watches the little ones and orders them around. I don't think the little ones are even alive. They're not living beings. They could be robots. They're having trouble with the laces on my boots … I know it's about to start!" I'm softly crying again.

"What's about to start Terry?"

"The examination. They do medical things and hurt me while I'm on the table. I fill my lungs with air to scream and nothing comes out again. Oh God, help me please! There's a tall one there. Don't look at me. Oh, God he's going to look at me!"

Sensing my anxiety Brad squeezed my hand and said softly, "Relax now Terry, and tell me about the tall one... he can't hurt you now. Tell me about him."

"He's not benign or malevolent. If he could talk he'd say, 'Nothing personal, just doing my job man.' He's a different type of entity, a different animal entirely. He's insect like and as tall as the aliens. The grey ones are their drones to do his bidding and help him. They are worker bees."

"What does the insect thing want with you?" Brad asked.

"I think they are trying to learn our anatomy. Learn how we work. They show no empathy whatsoever and just go about their business. They hurt me with instruments and mechanical stainless-steel probes and knives. There are tools that hang from a low domed ceiling. Everything is white porcelain or stainless steel. I'm restrained, and they did medical things to me. I tried to tell them I wasn't anesthetized. I was less than a human being, I was their lab rat. Then they make me forget ... and everything will be okay."

"Go on Terry."

"If someone hurts you Brad. If they hurt you and scare you but then make you forget it ever happened, does that make it okay? I think it's cruelty. These goddamn things are cruel! They hurt me, and I hate them all."

Brad asked, "Will they talk to you?"

"I try to talk to them every time. I want them to know I'm a living person aware of things and I can feel pain. They just ignore me. He was doing something to my chest and it hurt like hell. I remember screaming and cursing. I think he became annoyed with my screaming."

"What makes you think you annoyed him?" Brad wanted to know.

"I heard his voice inside my head. I heard it as clearly as any spoken word. He told me I had to stop screaming. He said, 'You know us. We will not harm you. You will go back, and you will not remember so why do you scream?' He touched my right temple again and I immediately lost consciousness until they took me back." I said.

I'm quiet again. My heart is still pounding. I'm watching various scenes play out in my head. So many things I didn't remember. These are the things the aliens made me forget.

Brad comforted me. There was a short pause. He squeezed my hand and told me, "You have done very well. But you must go back again to the tent. After they finish with you on the table what happens next? Just watch it in your mind Terry. Tell me what you're seeing."

"We're back in the tent now. We were somehow placed on the ground near the car instead of back in the tent! Somebody screwed up. So, they had to carry us back. They put us back in the tent. Toby first and then me. I was barely conscious. I remember a lot of pain. When they were satisfied with the way we were positioned, they left us. I lost consciousness as soon as they placed me on my air mattress."

"What happened next, Terry?"

"I woke up and saw Toby on his knees. He was staring out of the tent at something. I remember feeling confused when I woke up. We were both in a lot of pain. We watched them leave. Some of the little ones were still in the meadow and they had to walk into the beam."

"Terry, tell me what you saw when the little ones walked into the light?"

"We watched them from the tent, they walked into the light and then dissolved into it. The ship rose up in the air like a hot air balloon. Then the corners changed color to all white."

"Good, that's very good." Brad paused for a moment. "Terry, this is very important. You enjoy photography, don't you?"

"Yes Brad, I enjoy photography." I knew where this was headed. They think I took photographs of the spaceship and kept them secret. God, I wish I had. Again, I cursed myself for forgetting that camera. But who's to say it would have made a difference?

"You have a darkroom at home too, is that true?"

"Yes Brad, I have a darkroom, but only for black and white pictures."

"Terry, have you ever taken pictures of the B52s or the nuclear sites? If you tell me, know we can fix things and you won't be in trouble!"

I paused. I needed to concentrate, I remembered the photograph of Kilo-5 I took back in 1975, a couple months after the "black diamond" incident. I knew they didn't find it when they raided our home. The photograph itself wasn't a big deal but it would be hard to explain the "why." The launch facility was located off a state highway and visible to the public. I had blurted out so many things involuntarily. I was terrified of what I may have told Brad. My pause was too long for Brad's taste.

"Terry! Have you ever taken a picture at a site where photography is prohibited?"

I shot back without hesitation this time, "No Brad!"

He seemed satisfied with my answer and moved along.

"Terry, did you tell agent Gregory the whole truth about your camping trip with Toby at Devils Den? Did you tell the truth about your cameras and film?"

"Yes Brad, Toby had a little camera and he never used it. Everything I told Gregory was the truth." I could sense we were almost finished. I was terrified by the thought of what they might do to me or how this might end. Brad had warned me that if I wasn't fully cooperative, "this could end badly."

"Terry, have you lied to me or to the agents about anything you saw or did while you were on your camping trip?"

"No Brad." I had my wits about me again. The effects of the medicine must have been wearing off. I was careful not to betray my hypnotic posture.

I heard Brad ask the agents, "You boys good?"

Gregory spoke for the pair, "We're good, wrap it up Brad," I also heard the captain say something funny and everyone laughed for a quick moment.

Brad then turned his attention back to me.

"You've done a very good job Terry! Now I'm going to make it all go away. Would you like that? You'll be at peace."

"Yes Brad." I'm on autopilot again. I thought, No! No way will I forget this. Now, I knew what happened to me at Devils Den. This was information I owned.

"Terry, in just a moment I'll take these ugly memories away forever. You will forget everything that happened to you at Devils Den. You will forget that big ship and the aquariums, the men in tan uniforms with orange insignias. You will forget your trip to the moon, the things you saw and the things you were told about the moon. You will forget everything that happened to you at Devils Den and you will forget everything that happened to Toby. Ready?"

"Yes Brad."

Brad resumed humming. He removed the adhesive bandage from my arm. I felt him swab my arm and I could smell rubbing alcohol. He cleaned up the injection site so there would be no trace. He carefully rolled down the sleeve of my shirt and rebuttoned it.

Brad said, "Listen! You and Toby went on a camping trip to Devils Den and it was a horrible trip! You both were bug-bitten and sick, but that's all over now! When you recall what we did here today, all you will remember is our pleasant chat about camping, St Louis and photography. UFOs and space people don't exist! There is nothing on the moon but rocks! The tiny woman who was kind to you, you will forget about her. She was just a dream. Everything you saw or heard at Devils Den you will forget. It will be gone … and you won't be able to remember any of it, no matter how hard you try!"

"Yes Brad, I understand." Now I am terrified.

"Now listen to my voice, Terry. Remember when we walked down those ten stairs and you turned on that light by pulling that chain? Remember, we turned on the light to look around?"

"Yes Brad, I remember."

"We're all finished now! But before you can come back upstairs you'll need to pull the chain to turn out that light. When you pull that chain and the light goes out, all those memories will be gone forever." He repeated himself once more, word for word. Then, "Terry, you won't be able to remember them no matter how hard you try. Ready?"

"Yes Brad." What's really going to happen when I reach up and pull his imaginary chain? I reasoned that if Brad had control of my mind he'd have control of my arm too. I also deduced, if my arm responds to Brad's command automatically, then I probably will forget everything. But, if I need to voluntarily reach up like I did when I turned it on, maybe I'll be able to keep some or all of what just occurred.

"Now Terry! Now reach up and pull that chain and turn out that light! We're finished down here and it's time come back upstairs! Now reach up and grab that chain!"

Nothing happened! I waited to see if my arm would respond of its own volition. It didn't! I felt no compulsion to move my arm at all. I wanted to be certain that when I reached up and pulled that imaginary chain it would be my conscious act. The room was quiet. I didn't move. I knew Brad was growing anxious. I knew he'd repeat himself. I waited.

Then it came. Brad repeated his command, "Now Terry, reach up and turn off that light!"

This time I responded to Brad. I reached into the air like I did when we began. I mimicked pulling a faux chain. Then I let my arm slowly fall into my lap. I did a quick mental assessment.

There were gaps in the interrogation. But those were mostly early on when the medication's effect was at its strongest. I kept my memories and many new ones too! I knew we were close, but I knew we weren't finished. Not yet.

"Now Terry, walk up those stairs with me! Here we go! With each step feeling more alert. Ten, nine, eight, feeling more awake now

..., four and feeling alert, three, two and one! Wake up Terry. Open your eyes feeling rested and feeling great. Now take a big stretch."

Very consciously and deliberately I opened my eyes, but I wasn't feeling great. I had been in that same position for hours, it felt good to stretch. It felt even better knowing this nightmare might finally end today. I noticed the agents were packing up their paperwork. There was a positive vibe in the room.

The major's little kit was under his arm. Without a word, he left the room. I know this will sound crazy and I don't know why but I expected a goodbye.

Briefcase in hand, Gregory said, "Finish out your enlistment and go to college, son. There's nothing on your record to worry about so long as you keep your mouth shut. You do understand the rules? You cannot talk about anything pertaining to your camping trip. That all ended here today. It's nobody's business. Am I getting through to you?"

"Yes sir, I don't remember much about it anyway," I said, purely for Gregory's benefit.

Gregory was cordial, "Your old CO asked me speak with you. The hospital's down a couple people. They could use you. But you'll be on day shift. Would you like to return to the hospital squadron?"

"Sir, I'd like to work as an EMT again. If I can go back, it would make me very happy, sir."

"Son, I'm not in the business of making people happy. Those orders will be cut this week. The driver will take you home. You can take the rest of the day off. I cleared it with your CO. Be careful what you photograph with that telescopic lens of yours."

"Yes sir." With that, I was gone. He opened the door for me and left! I wanted to skip going down the hall like a ten-year-old. I was singing a song under my breath. One we used to sing in the schoolyard when I was about six or seven, "I know something you don't know, I know something you don't know!"

They knew about the space people. The agents knew. They might even work for them or whoever is in their alien chain of command. I do know something they don't!

I recalled what Gregory told me when I called him that day and offered to take a polygraph test. He said he wasn't interested. He said, "I have my own lie-detector, son." I think I just met his lie-detector.

If the purpose of this exercise was to wipe my memory clean, they failed. They failed, and they don't even know it. Thanks to Brad, I know so much more. Now it made sense. Brad confirmed alien abduction, alien apathy and alien amnesia. I'd had a dose of it all.

Those memories and the images that Brad's failed hypnotic session pulled into my conscious mind are mine now. I kept them too. They're tucked away in a little compartment inside my head. I knew I could keep them, most of them. What I didn't know was that they came with a heavy price.

Betty, the Lady MIB

Since the device in my leg was discovered back in 2012, memories of Devils Den have returned to my conscious mind. I sometimes wonder how different my life would be had I not resisted Brad's promise to take those memories away? I may have missed the opportunity to surrender this madness into his hands.

I fought so hard to keep these memories because I own them, and I believed I could live with them. I was half-right. I learned early on that whenever I visit that night at Devils Den, the horror of it all returns. Like I told Brad back in 1977, "These beings have rules," and I opted to stay in the game.

My wife and I have been programmed to avoid the topic. Like Pavlov's famous experiments with dogs, my wife and I are conditioned to avoid the topic because it causes us pain. We recognize the terror that always accompanies those memories. For forty years I had managed to keep the door to that compartment in my mind on lock-down.

The awareness of this object in my knee kicked-down the door to that compartment. It's like the memories that come back to you when you page through your high school yearbook. You see people and things you hadn't thought about in years or maybe decades. Images you probably could never have recalled regardless of how hard you tried. You've heard the saying that, "something jogged my memory?" The right cue or trigger and the memories return. It works because memories never go away. They lie dormant, just underneath the skin like this thing in my leg.

Seeing the implants on film was the visual cue that triggered a response in my brain. Memories returned first as nightmares and eventually they seeped into my waking consciousness. Some things spontaneously returned to my awareness. Many came roaring back as horrific nightmares. The kind of nightmare you wake from screaming. This is not fantasy or hallucination. I recalled real events from the past. Everything that returned to my conscious memory dovetailed with what I could recall. Everything fits. Often, one dream would pick-up where the previous dream ended.

Reviewing my notebooks brought back more terror and pain. The suffering was necessary to document everything. By journaling and writing I can both process these things and preserve them too. They are important. People need to know the truth. Alien entities are real, and we are all at risk of abduction or worse. Then there's the "agenda."

In late 2016 a new consequence came out of the darkness. I started to lose weight. The weight loss coincides with my decision to aggressively tell all that I know. Since I quit running in 2005 my weight went from my usual 190 lbs. to 240 lbs. and stayed. I carried an extra fifty pounds, but I was otherwise healthy. I'm now down to 150 lbs. It's a daily battle to keep my weight above 150 lbs. What concerns my doctor is what she refers to as a wasting of muscle. I'm now frail and vulnerable.

In 2013, I was duty-bound to find Tobias. Instinctually I knew Toby's testimony would bolster my own. I was far too late. He succumbed to alcoholism and the injuries he likely suffered at the hands of extraterrestrial beings and their co-conspirators.

That bucket of pills they sent home with us back in 1977 has always troubled me. I'm grateful for my wife's keen observation and her ability to make the connection between my sudden memory problems and the unmarked pills. Thanks to her, I only took them for three days and flushed the remaining eleven days down the toilet.

If Toby had taken all fourteen days as prescribed what kind of effects could it have had on his psyche? I believe Toby also suffered worse treatment during the abduction. Like he said, "They hurt us Terry." I could see the pain behind those bloodshot eyes. "Yeah Tobe," they did hurt us. I believe Toby's obsession with the sky was a result of being abducted as a child. The loss of Toby's life made this project important on a personal level. It cost Toby the life he never had an opportunity to live. I want the world to know.

Although most of the past 40 or so years have been peaceful I was still tagged. Like research animal in the wild, sometime in my past I'd been abducted and hopefully rendered unconscious while the ugly praying-mantis creature implanted their devices in my leg. How much of my life has been studied, monitored and even manipulated by them?

My wife and a few trusted friends thought it would be wise to explore all possible explanations before labeling the metal device in my leg as paranormal. Friends pointed out that perhaps my films were accidentally switched in the emergency room. Maybe the x-rays I had belonged to someone else?

My wife and I knew that explanation wasn't possible. I discussed and viewed my x-rays at the hospital in real time. Instead of the routine two x-rays they took eight shots of my knee and asked a radiologist to view the films in my presence. These x-rays belong to me and are of no one else.

That left just one remote possibility. It's rare but it's not paranormal.

We've all heard stories about combat veterans who 50 years after battle cough up a bullet. That fact was easy to verify. It really does happen on rare occasions. Is it possible that as a child I swallowed this object? Could this thing, over 60 years have migrated from my digestive tract into my thigh just above my knee?

I had two possible explanations left. It was either a piece of metal I swallowed at some point in my life and it worked its way into my knee over the years. Or, it had been intentionally and covertly implanted in my knee using some method not recognized by modern medicine. Either by alien beings or maybe even by the USAF. I needed help from a medical professional. Fortunately, I knew someone.

The best candidate for my question was a friend back in Vermont. She's a board-certified radiologist who expressed interest in my knee; she asked that I protect her anonymity for the sake of her reputation in the medical community. I understand the stigma that goes with the topic. At her request I'll refer to as Dr. Hong.

She agreed to see me, and I paid the airfare for the flight to Burlington, Vermont. I showed her my 2012 x-rays and explained that there was no visible scar. I was totally candid with her. She understood the implications of what I was alleging. Before expressing her opinion, she insisted that she should examine my knee. After a thorough examination she kindly explained.

"Mr. Lovelace, I'm not an expert in these matters. I don't know anyone who is. But I can't reconcile these x-rays and your knee. Could these x-rays belong to someone else?"

I explained that possibility had been ruled out at the VA Hospital. These x-rays belong to my knee.

"Whatever these artifacts might be, they were inserted into your thigh by methods unknown to medical science. It got inside your thigh without breaching the surface of your skin. There is absolutely zero probability that you swallowed an object that eventually worked its way to your leg. The digestive tract is a closed system."

I thanked her and paid her. Now, I am 100% certain by the weight of the evidence that during my life, a non-human entity implanted this object in my right knee. It could have been done any time prior to 2012. I think it's likely the cause of the "numb spot" that I experienced as a runner.

There is another fact worth mentioning. There are others with experiences nearly identical to mine. Our stories are incredibly similar. Every story I've researched regarding people who've been found to carry implants share two things common. First, they all claim to have experienced an abduction or other unique UFO interaction. Second, by chance they all discovered an object under their skin on x-ray without a corresponding scar.

Many credible people have stepped forward with unbelievable stories about alien abduction. But the world is little different today than it was when Betty and Barney Hill took that drive home through rural New Hampshire. In some small measure, I hope to change that.

Carl Sagan's observation was so true, "Incredible claims require incredible proof." Proof of alien contact that will stand-up to the peer review process is just not going to happen until our government agrees to it. It's in their control or the control of their overlords.

If our government is sincere about its search for extraterrestrial life, why do they limit their search to listening for radio waves and searching for planets in distant galaxies? If they were genuinely interested in proof, why let thousands of police reports and witness statements rot in file cabinets across the country? As I said at the onset, our government wants the public to focus on far away galaxies. It's the events close to home that make them uncomfortable.

Why? I know three answers that make sense. In the law there are differing standards of proof to establish your assertion and win the case. Everyone knows to prove someone guilty of murder the standard of proof is beyond a reasonable doubt. In most civil matters the standard is to prove that your assertion is more likely than not, or sometimes referred to as, "51% vs. 49%". One standard of proof is by the weight of the evidence. The weight of the evidence over the past 60 years is more than enough to prove that extraterrestrial beings exist, and they visit our planet. A lot. They capture people and implant devices in them. It's an incredible claim but it's true and provable by the weight of the evidence.

If I were to take the case for extraterrestrial life visiting earth to a trial by jury I'm confident I could prove my case by the weight of the evidence.

So why does our government and governments globally turn a blind eye? I have three possible scenarios I'd ask you to consider: (1) There may be a quid pro quo arrangement. In exchange for technology we grant them permission to pursue their limited agenda without interference, or (2) Our government is working in concert shoulder-to-shoulder with alien beings toward a shared goal, or lastly (3) Our government is incapable of stopping alien beings from abducting people. In that case the government's role is to mitigate collateral damage and control public fear. Any one of these three scenarios are good reason to shift public attention to the search for distant planets and radio waves.

The topic of alien implants is the butt of jokes and fodder for comedians. But devices implanted in people are sometimes recovered. I'm not unique. Alien implants have been discovered by happenstance like mine. A few were surgically recovered for laboratory analysis.

A podiatrist from California named Dr. Roger Leir recovered several from men and women until his death in 2014. He was a brave man and suffered ridicule in the medical colleagues. All his patients claimed to have been a victim of alien abduction or had experienced lost time. When Leir recovered implants, they were analyzed and found to be composed of exotic material. Some of the metals were found to exist on earth only in meteorites. Some were of hitherto unknown elements that will remain unknown because they were never shared within the scientific community.

In early 2016, I began gathering drawings and journals from 1977 forward. Sheila too, had chronicled occurrences between 1977 through 1987 in diaries of her own. Fortunately, she had the forethought to safely store everything that we'd chronicled. In our storage locker she found the sketches I drew in 1977 through 1979 that we both thought had been lost.

The nightmares began in early 2013 after the discovery of the implants. They began in earnest immediately after I made a public appearance at a September 2017 UFO conference in Houston. The real consequence would come a month later. It would be epic.

It arrived on a Friday evening. My wife and I went out for dinner and saw a movie. I don't recall what we watched but it wasn't anything in the horror or science fiction genre. It was a pleasant evening and we were home by around 11:00 PM.

I performed my usual nighttime ritual of locking things up and setting the alarm. I made it to bed a little before midnight and fell soundly asleep for what felt like just an instant.

When I opened my eyes, I found myself in our family room! I was seated upright in my chair and sweating profusely. I could see the alarm panel from my chair. The alarm was set and had not been triggered. Never in my life have I walked in my sleep. Not once.

Seated directly across from me is what I first mistook to be a small Asian woman. I would estimate her height at four feet. She wore oversized sunglasses that hid her large almond eyes and part of her face. She wore a red headscarf she had loosely tied to hide her pencil thin neck. Aside from the red scarf she was dressed all in black. Black blouse buttoned to the top with long sleeves that partially hid the four very long digits. Her pants and shoes were also black. She sat casually with a non-threatening posture.

My first thought was the "men in black" or the MIB who supposedly confronted people who've had UFO experiences. Their alleged goal is to dissuade witnesses from telling others about their experience. Honestly, I thought the MIB stories were urban legend and just a movie plot. But even urban legends sometimes have a kernel of truth.

I felt mildly sedated. The house was silent except for my breathing. I caught that strange ionized scent in the air and the hair on my arms stood up. I thought to callout for my wife, but I knew she wouldn't wake up. They make sure of that too.

I recalled that in 1987 my wife woke up to find a tiny woman standing at the edge of our bed. She spoke telepathically and told her, "Everything is okay, go back to sleep." An entity, possibly the same entity now sitting across from me may have visited our home in 1987 and never tripped the alarm or disturbed the dog. I guess I shouldn't be surprised to find her in my home a second time.

She wore a wig. It was an outdated style with jet-black hair sitting slightly askew on top of her head. From a silhouette her hair reminded me of the cartoon character from the Flintstone cartoons of the 60s, "Betty Rubble." I couldn't help but think, "That wig looks ridiculous!"

She immediately replied, telepathically. I heard her clearly inside my skull and her voice was familiar.

"So, you don't like my hair? It's the same."

"The same as what?" I thought.

"The same as the last time we met."

I heard her, but her lips never moved. I'd forgotten. They communicate telepathically. That was their method of communication. My unspoken comment had hurt her feelings.

"No, no I'm just shocked and scared… that's all, scared." I felt compelled to add, "It looks very nice."

She seemed to acknowledge my apology.

This was beyond surreal. I was in my own home sitting across from a half human and half alien being while my wife slept just down hallway. This was the same being I encountered a long time ago. That didn't change the fact that I was scared out of my wits. I hoped to escape without being abducted again and subjected to another one of their torturous examinations.

Then it registered! It struck me like a bolt of lightning. That 1987 motorcycle ride when I lost two hours of time! They abducted me from that gravel farm-road. Ten years earlier at Devils Den I was taken for the umpteenth time with poor Toby along for the ride. I remembered, or should I say they allowed me to remember those things. I was certain I met her during that abduction and probably a long time before that.

The voice I heard in my head came as plainly as a spoken word. She spoke with perfect English grammar with no discernable accent. She responded to my thoughts immediately, "Yes, I'm *that* woman. No, you will not be taken tonight. No more examinations, ever. I promise."

Her promise ebbed my fear by a degree. Very soon all my fears had vanished. I wasn't surprised.

I stared at her and recognized her face. I recognized her voice too. I was amazed that she hadn't aged since I last saw her in 1987. Her body shape and facial structure were identical to the woman I met in 1987. As I stared at her I picked-up more human features in her face. She impressed me as a hybrid being made up of one-half human and one-half alien. I assume that's true because she didn't correct me.

She was aware that I was still trying to deal with her appearance. I wanted to see more of her face.

She removed her sunglasses and revealed her large almond shaped eyes. They were black and not as large as what they portray in the exaggerated pictures in the media. Despite the familiarity I was shocked by her appearance. She was not a human being. She was something else and that was disturbing.

My mind raced. Why is this woman in my home? Did she intend to harm me because I spoke openly about my experiences?

Of course, she intercepted those thoughts and reassured me she would not harm me. But she stated that my public disclosures and writing a book for publication was worrisome to both her hosts and to my government.

She knew what I was thinking. It was hard to process. I remember in elementary school; a teacher once asked the class to not think about elephants. Of course, everyone could think of nothing but elephants. Controlling our own thoughts is not as easy as it sounds. I was afraid a wrong thought could have terrible consequences.

For that reason, I thought it was important to address the issue of privacy. Directing my thought toward her I registered my concern, "I'm accustomed to my thoughts being private and not open for others to know unless I choose to do so. Some thoughts are my own and I may not wish to share them with others."

She replied as I finished the sentence. "Yes, you can have privacy. You can keep some of your thoughts private, Terry. Just try."

I was moved by the fact she used my name. But, I was unsure if she was telling me the truth or just placating me? It was evident that she didn't require time to compose her thoughts. Every time, her reply immediately followed my last word.

She added, "You already know how to keep things separated in your mind. You already know how to keep some thoughts private. You can do so if you wish to."

"I'll try."

"Terry, I am here because you have memories that cannot be permanently suppressed or removed safely from your mind. Because those memories cannot be erased, you intend to tell others to help you manage these unwelcome thoughts. By telling others you hope to confirm your experiences and make people aware."

"I agree. But what could I know that is so important? Lots of people write books and openly discuss their experiences. Why am I singled out?"

She was unequivocal, "You know things and you have seen images of things that are crucial to their shared agenda. They are important to both your government and to my hosts. You are not aware of their importance and you can't discern which memories are sensitive and should not be disclosed. To remove them now would cause you great harm."

It was difficult to stay on topic. I asked, "Is this thing in my leg tied to all of this? How many people have been tagged with an implant like mine?" I wanted to know but I wasn't prepared for the answer.

"Many, many thousands over three generations," was her reply.

I was stunned by her answer. I asked her, "Please answer two questions for me. What is the purpose of this thing in my leg? Are you here to persuade me to not disclose what I know?"

Her answers continued to astonish me, "You have devices in both of your legs. They serve a purpose and they have caused you no harm. If you continue to speak publicly and if you publish your book, my hosts will recover them. That is the limit of my hosts' concern."

Then it occurred to me! My left leg had never been x-rayed. I have two of these things inside of me! My next thought was, "Why … how can the devices be removed?"

"My hosts will not allow you to have them removed here and analyzed by terrestrial scientist for their composition. They won't harm you and you'll experience no pain. They'll remove them from your body while you're sleeping. Your government also has interests in you and in your devices," she added.

I asked, "I still don't understand. Can you answer plainly? These things in my leg, what purpose do they serve?"

"The devices have many purposes. The concern among all is that once disclosed they will support your claims. Your government will not allow it. They will first attempt to discredit you," she said with emphasis.

"Who are your hosts?" I asked. It seemed like such an odd way to refer to whatever entities she worked for. "Host" can be a verb as in to "host" a dinner party. It can also be used to reference a symbiotic relationship that can be mutualistic or parasitic.

She gave an eloquent reply, "You call them aliens. I refer to them as my hosts because they are not alien to me."

With that question answered I asked again, "A lot of people write books, speak in public and in the media on the topic of extraterrestrial beings visiting earth! Why would my government not allow me to disclose these things? Why is my information any different?"

She didn't reply but nodded her head.

What happened next was a graphic replay of four scenes from my past. I could see four vignettes play-out in my mind's eye. Each scene was a concise episode of a life event. It played-out in color graphics and the quotes spoken in my own voice. I was outside myself as an observer from behind and above.

It was very much like the images Major Brownfield a/k/a Brad pulled up and into my conscious memory under my semi-hypnosis session. These were not my thoughts and I could not control what was happening in each scene. Each scene lasted only 60 or so seconds. I was amazed at how much she could convey in just a few short minutes.

In the first scene I was seated in the interrogation room at the OSI building on Whiteman AFB back in 1977. I watched myself telling Brad about the ships dimensions and its interior. I told him that it was so huge it could never fly across the side of the moon that faces the earth. Then a memory I hadn't disclosed to Brad. Inside the big ship there were human men and women in tan uniforms with red insignias. They ignored us completely and went about their business. It was plane to see they were members of the ship's crew in some capacity. Next, I saw myself seated at my kitchen table drawing pictures of the large ship.

In the second vignette I saw myself inside the very large ship. There's a petite woman by my side and we were talking, exchanging thoughts. I held my motorcycle helmet in my right hand by its strap. It is the same woman sitting across from me! We are looking through a giant window at a jet-black sky with a billion stars. It was breathtaking. I felt we must be in a large warehouse of some kind. I never experienced the slightest sensation of motion. Then from the right side of the panel the moon rolled into my view. It was huge. We were no more than 30,000 feet above it I'd later estimate. At that moment I thought, "It's going to hit us!" Betty then assured me we were moving, not the moon. She explained we were onboard a ship and all was well.

The sliver of moon I saw in front of us was the edge of bright side, glowing greyish-white. The ship turned, and we traveled into the dark side. We travelled some distance and everything in front of us was black. The stars were no longer visible there was only darkness. This was the dark side of the moon and we had turned to face the surface. Soon, I saw specks of light on the surface below us. There were more and more lights spread across the darkened landscape. We were closer, and buildings were clearly visible. It was an entire city. It was a huge sprawling complex. It was akin to the view from a commercial airliner on a landing approach over LAX at night! The randomness of the buildings was confusing for a moment. Something looked out of place. Then it struck me, the city looked odd because there were no roads or streets. There were no parking lots or vehicles. Just a large collection of randomly scattered structures. Many of the buildings had square windows and the interiors were well lit.

I was fascinated by the view below. She said the ship we were in was too large to land on the moon. She told me there were human beings living and working on the moon. In this vignette our dialogue in 1987 went as follows.

I asked, "Human beings are living here? How long have we been here?"

"For many decades," she said matter-of-factly. She said they were, "There to collect and process the rocks."

This ended vignettes one and two. These are the two things I she warned me not to disclose for my safety. The third I've explained as relevant only between my wife and I. Whatever importance there may be in that fourth scene above my level of understanding,

I have shared the content of Betty's warning with my wife and editor, but no one else. The information will be released if I abruptly die or meet some unfortunate end. I thought it was prudent to do so considering my health.

She gave me just those four "chapters" presented without commentary and received by me as a gift. I'm certain these were not random thoughts, dreams, or hallucinations. These came directly from her mind to mine. I believe this was her way to tell me not to publish. Further, not to openly discuss alien visitation, alien hybrid and human involvement openly. I believe the sensitive information concerns humans living on the moon, the "big ship" and the collecting and processing of rocks. That's all she shared.

The questions I asked her were rarely the ones I would have chosen if I'd been given time to think through what she said before composing my next question.

She then said words that still haunt me, "Your government will kill you."

I should have asked so much more but I was numb. In the minute or two it took me to regain my composure the scene went to black.

I woke up in the living room chair at dawn. I walked to my office and recorded as much as I could remember. Then I went back to bed and slept soundly until noon.

I do my best to not dwell on what she told me. It would be too easy to obsess. I go about my daily activity and choke the memories down. I read the news and wonder where our civilization is headed. I write and publish my book, so others will know this stuff is real. Our government, world governments, have kept us in the dark far too long.

I am writing a second book. My wife suggested writing 40+ years ago to cope with the alien interactions in my life. It was helpful for me back then. It is helpful for me today.

The words, "If you tell … they will kill you," worry me some, but not enough to deter my efforts. I feel the more exposure I have the safer I am.

After her appearance I went to work with a newfound urgency. It was more important than ever to record everything I knew. And make it accessible to the public.

There's no way I'll ever know how much was hidden from me. Betty was very clear about a couple things. Her claim that the devices I carry in both legs would be removed by her hosts. Less than a month later they came calling and retrieved their property while I slept.

I woke up on November 16, 2017 with pain in both of my legs between my knee and my groin. Twenty-four hours later the bruises appeared and the pain in my legs made walking difficult. With help from my wife, we photographed my legs. The wound in the center of the bruising looked like insect bites. When photographed and enlarged they were box shaped clearly distinguishable from an insect bite. From what I know about human anatomy nothing in the human body has 45-degree angles and straight lines.

On the morning of November 18th, I set out to get my legs x-rayed. That proved to be more difficult than I ever imagined. Hospital x-ray facilities require an order from a staff physician. My physician friends were spread out between Michigan, Vermont, and American Samoa. Free-standing imaging centers not associated with a hospital likewise require a doctor's order.

On a long shot I stopped by a chiropractic office without an appointment. After a 45-minute wait he offered to speak to me. He was initially disinterested. Then he glanced at the x-ray I held up to his face as he was escorting me to the door. He stopped dead in his tracks.

Staring at the x-ray for a minute or so he invited me into his office and asked me to tell him the condensed story. I did, and he listened. He listened for 45 minutes despite his phone ringing and urgent knocks on his office door.

He wrote a prescription for an x-ray and told me where to go. No payment required but he did ask to see a copy of the films.

Two hours later I was home and holding the x-ray film up to the sunlight pouring through my kitchen window. Neither my wife nor I have enough knowledge to evaluate an x-ray, but it was clear the metal things were missing. On both sides of my legs they appeared to be gone. We found what Betty promised. Her hosts had reclaimed their property. They were gone. At least the metallic ones above the knee were gone.

Betty's hosts had visited me in the middle of the night and removed both devices from my upper legs. I guess I wasn't prepared for that. I should have been. She said they would remove them and attempt to discredit me.

In the morning I dropped the x-rays off for the chiropractor to see. He was busy with patients, so I left them at the front desk. I still didn't know where this development left me.

At five o'clock that evening my chiropractor friend called on my cell. "Well," he asked, "what do you think of your films?" I explained I didn't know whether to be elated or depressed.

He was upbeat, "The metallic objects are mostly gone from both legs. But the anomalies below the knee are still intact without change."

"Whoa, doctor. What exactly do you mean when you say they are *mostly gone*? The implants are gone from both legs ... but they failed to remove something?!"

"They did indeed. There are two tiny fragments of wire left behind. They are tiny, but they are plane to see. If you know where to look."

I couldn't believe it! He told me where to look and I was thrilled. There they were! Two tiny wires, side-by-side.

They had left something behind. It was my validation as much as a curtain tucked into the venetian blinds. I now had the proof I hoped for. I was wise to document the wounds on my legs. Those two pieces of wire left behind are the evidence to prove my case. Extraordinary claims require extraordinary proof. I have extraordinary proof in my right leg. Above and below my knee

I thanked my chiropractor friend and he declined payment. But he asked for a copy of my book. Of course, I promised him a copy.

I valued an opinion from a chiropractor; they look at dozens of x-rays daily. But I need solid confirmation from a board-certified radiologist. I bought a ticket to Burlington to see my friend Dr. Hong one more time. She was perfect because she had seen my "before" films. Now she'd see the "after."

Placing the new film on her light-box, she studied them for a moment. She was shocked to see the metallic object she documented earlier, was gone! This time she was looking for a scar where the metal devices had been removed. Faint bruises were still visible on my upper thigh. The small box-like wounds from the center of both petal-like patterns of bruising were still visible. They had mostly healed by then but were still somewhat squarely shaped.

Next, she turned her attention to the lower and lateral area of my right thigh. She looked for a that would be left had the object had been surgically removed. Of course, there was none. Next, because the wires are so tiny, she wanted to rule out intentional deception.

Apologetically, she explained, "If you implanted these yourself, or if someone else did it for you, a puncture wound would still be visible. I know where to look for evidence of a puncture that would correspond to the placement of the wires." Her examination of my legs took ten minutes.

There was no sign of a wound or puncture site anywhere on my thigh. After comparing both x-ray images closely, she said, "These are not film anomalies. These are consistent with the object in the original x-ray. It's my medical opinion that the metallic structure I saw in your in your 2012 x-ray is now gone. Further, there's no trace of a surgical incision to explain its removal. In its place now are two, tiny lengths of wire in deep muscle tissue in the right thigh. The round artifacts below the knee are unchanged. Mr. Lovelace, you have a very unusual knee."

"Yes Doctor. I've been told that before."

Betty and Barney Hill's famous interrupted ride through New Hampshire didn't change things. When I lived in Vermont, I'd travel that same stretch of road where the Hills were taken aboard a spaceship. But never at night. I did so probably once a year in silent reflection. I'm hopeful there will come change and disclosure very soon. More credible people in government positions like Mr. Hellyer will step-up and risk ridicule or worse to disclose the truth.

This is the way things stand as of 2018. I believe mankind has made some incredible discoveries they've managed to keep secret. Little by little we all work to reach that tipping point.

EPILOGUE

The question on everyone's mind is, "When can we expect disclosure from our government?" Never. The answer is never.

Oh, it's coming. But it'll manifest through a grass roots movement. You're a party to it already. *We are disclosure* my friends. Think, talk, read, argue and share. I know some of you will say, "If I can't see it with my own two eyes ... " That's okay. I'm not here to change your mind. I'm here to open your eyes. If you can just say, "There might be something to all this," that's enough! I understand. We've all been programed to deny, deny, deny ... "

If some of this resonates with you on a deeper level, I encourage you to be introspective. If you're struggling with intrusive thoughts, nightmares or worse, please, reach out to someone. Reach out to me. I'm not a therapist but if you'd like to share privately, I'll listen to you, reply, and help if I can. You can securely contact me at lovelace.landpope@gmail.com. I will respect your anonymity.

THE END

Photos

The author awaiting assignment to Whiteman Airforce Base 1973

Polaroid of Kilo-5 missile silo taken a few months after the sighting of the "black diamond" 1975

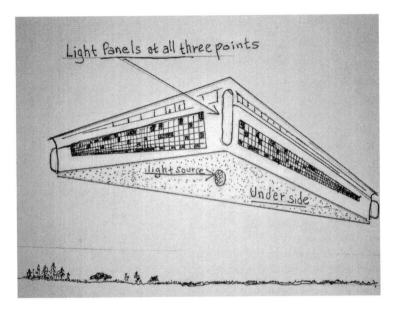

Redrawn by author from a sketch dated September 4th, 1977
Note: people, car, and tent shown for scale

Author drawn scene as viewed from a rear window of his home in August of 1978

Radiograph of author's thigh 2012

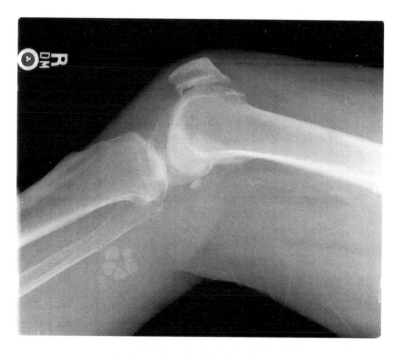

Radiograph of author's calf 2012

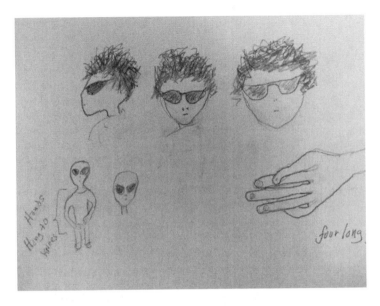

"Betty" the lady MIB drawn immediately following her visit October 2017

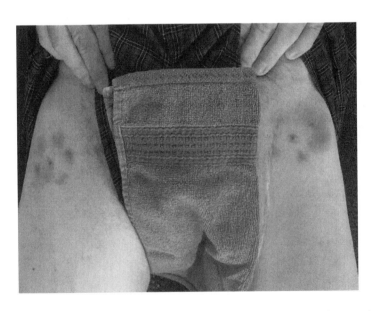

Author's thighs showing bruising and small square hole where metal anomaly was removed as "Betty" had promised less than a month previous November 16, 2017

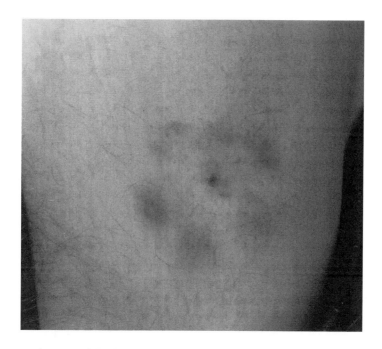

Close up of thigh bruises and square hole November 16, 2017

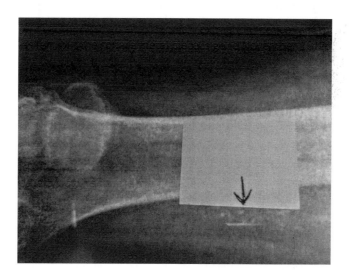

Radiograph of author's thigh after anomaly extraction, notice that the thin wire was left, but the square metal piece is gone November 16, 2017

Author as Assistant Attorney General of US Samoa Territory 2005

Author Terry Lovelace today as he works to keep his weight above 150 lbs. since his inexplicable and dramatic weight loss of nearly 80 lbs. over a 2-year period 2018

Printed in Great Britain
by Amazon